PRIMARY MATHEMATICS 1A
WORKBOOK

Anjolie

 Marshall Cavendish Education

 Singapore Math Inc®

Original edition published under the titles
Primary Mathematics Workbook 1A (Part One) and 1A (Part Two)
© 1981 Curriculum Planning & Development Division
Ministry of Education, Singapore
Published by Times Media Private Limited
This American Edition
© 2003 Times Media Private Limited
© 2003 Marshall Cavendish International (Singapore) Private Limited
© 2014 Marshall Cavendish Education Pte Ltd

Published by Marshall Cavendish Education
Times Centre, 1 New Industrial Road, Singapore 536196
Customer Service Hotline: (65) 6213 9444
US Office Tel: (1-914) 332 8888 | Fax: (1-914) 332 8882
E-mail: tmesales@mceducation.com
Website: www.mceducation.com

Singapore Math Inc.®
Distributed by
Singapore Math Inc.®
19535 SW 129th Avenue
Tualatin, OR 97062
U.S.A.
Website: www.singaporemath.com

First published 2003
Second impression 2003
Reprinted 2004 (twice)
Third impression 2005
Reprinted 2005 (twice), 2006 (twice), 2007 (twice), 2008, 2009,
        2010 (twice), 2011 (twice), 2012, 2013, 2014, 2015, 2016

ISBN 978-981-01-8496-4

Printed in Singapore

ACKNOWLEDGEMENTS

Our special thanks to Richard Askey, Professor of Mathematics (University of Wisconsin,
Madison), Yoram Sagher, Professor of Mathematics (University of Illinois, Chicago), and Madge
Goldman, President (Gabriella and Paul Rosenbaum Foundation), for their indispensable
advice and suggestions in the production of Primary Mathematics (U.S. Edition).

CONTENTS

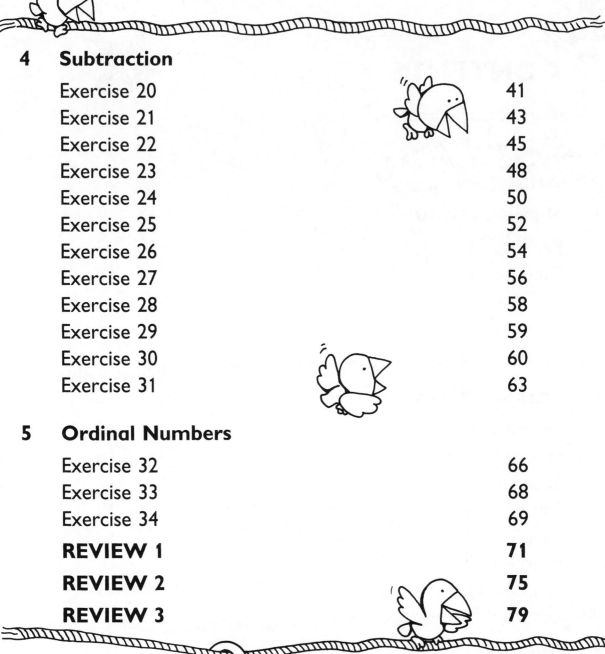

4 Subtraction

5 Ordinal Numbers

6   Numbers to 20

7   Shapes

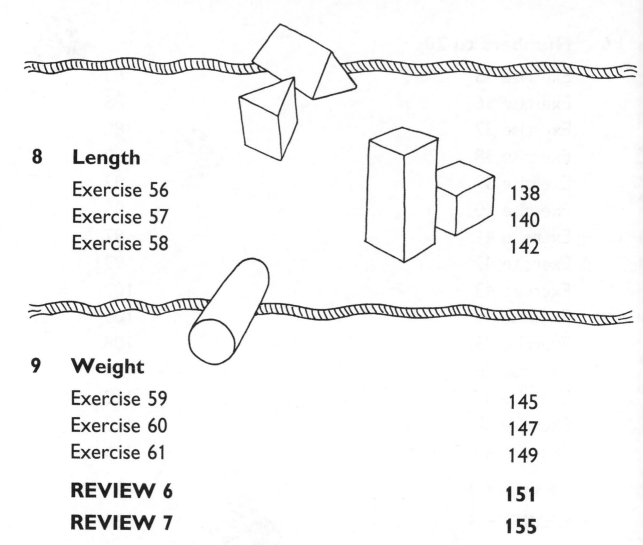

EXERCISE 1

1. Match.

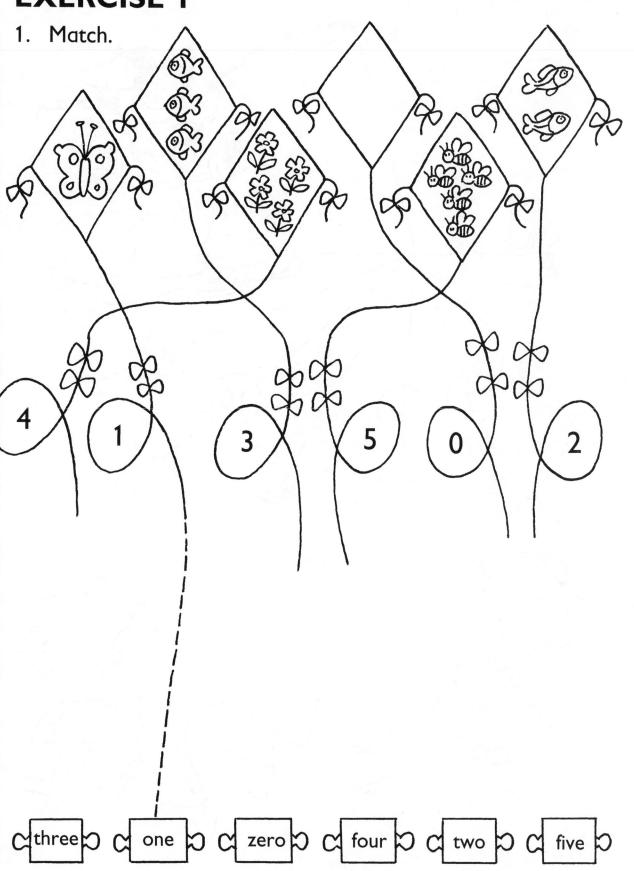

2. Match.

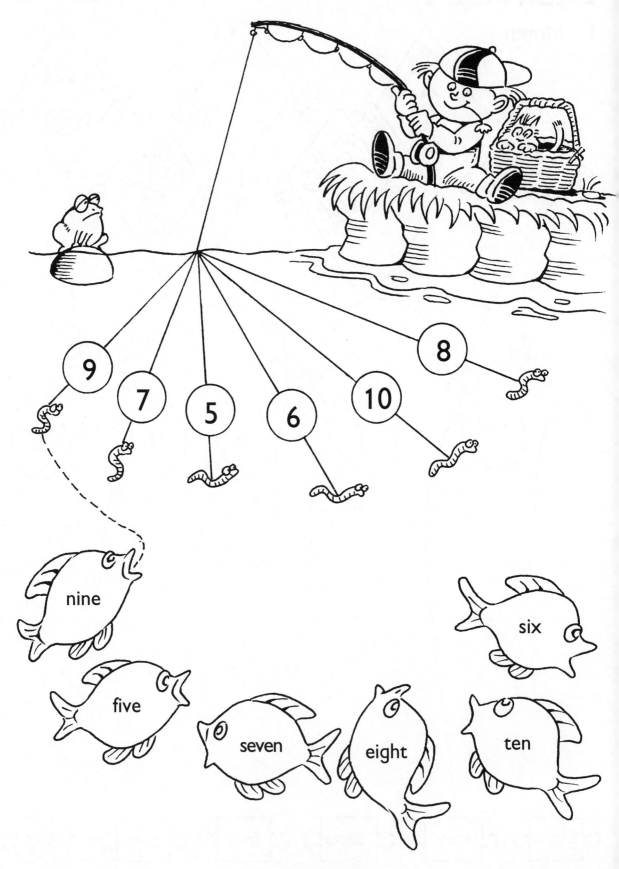

EXERCISE 2

1. Write the numbers.

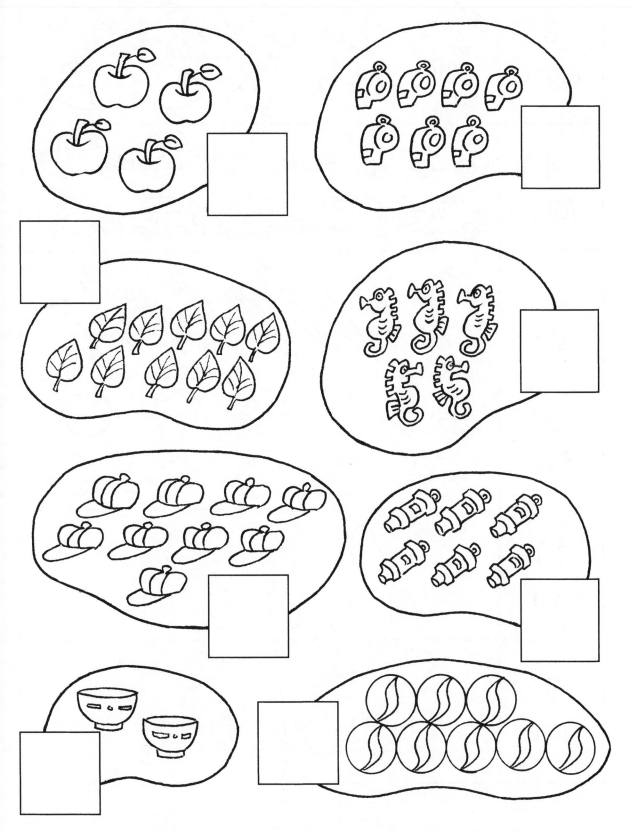

2. Color the correct number of objects.

8 eight	
4 four	
6 six	
5 five	
10 ten	
9 nine	

EXERCISE 3

1. Circle the two sets which have the same number of objects.

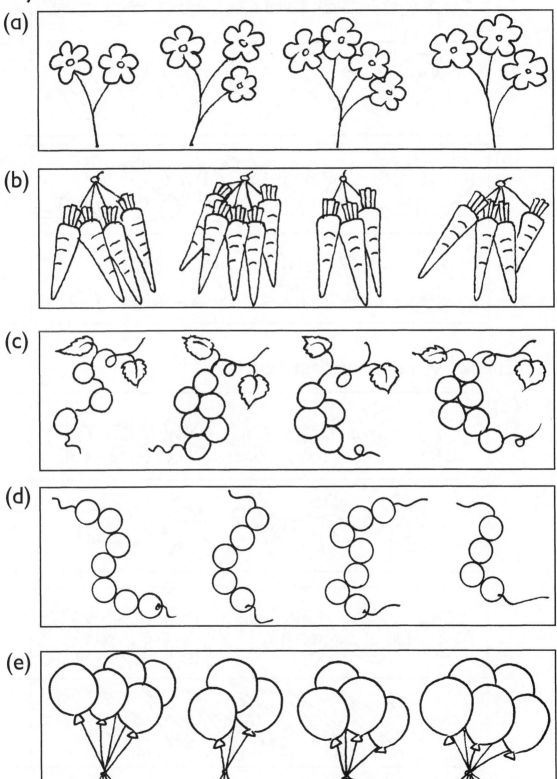

(a)

(b)

(c)

(d)

(e)

2. Check ✓ the set that has more.

(a)

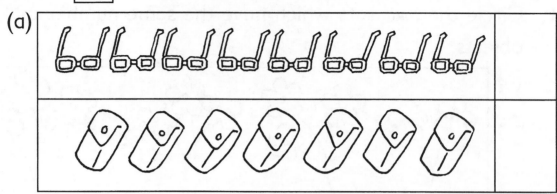

(b)

3. Check ✓ the set that has less.

(a)

(b)

EXERCISE 4

1. Join the dots in order. Begin with 1.

   (a)

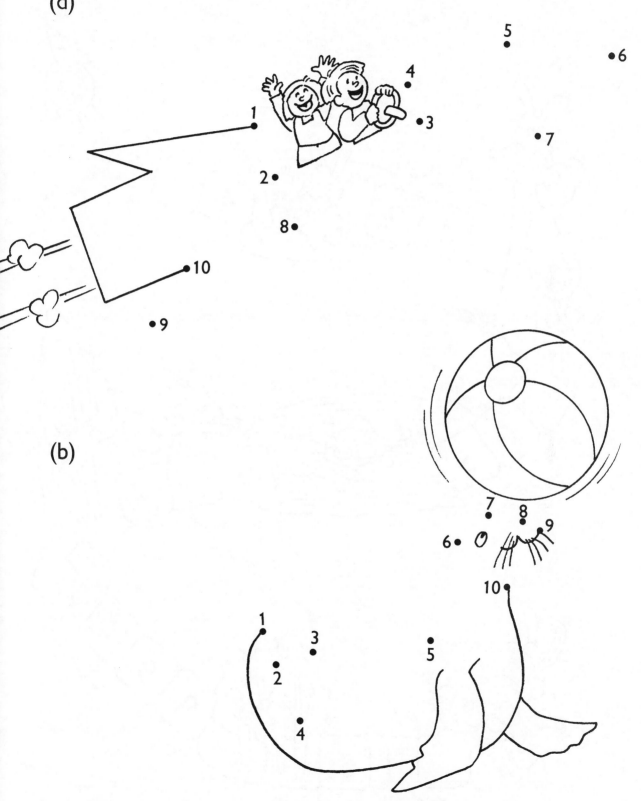

   (b)

2. Fill in the missing numbers.

EXERCISE 5

1. Color the things that Mr. Six likes.

The numbers on each pair should make 6.

EXERCISE 6

1. Help Mr. Seven to open the doors with the keys.

The numbers on the key and the door should make 7.

EXERCISE 7

1. Mr. Eight knocked down two pins in each set.

Color them.

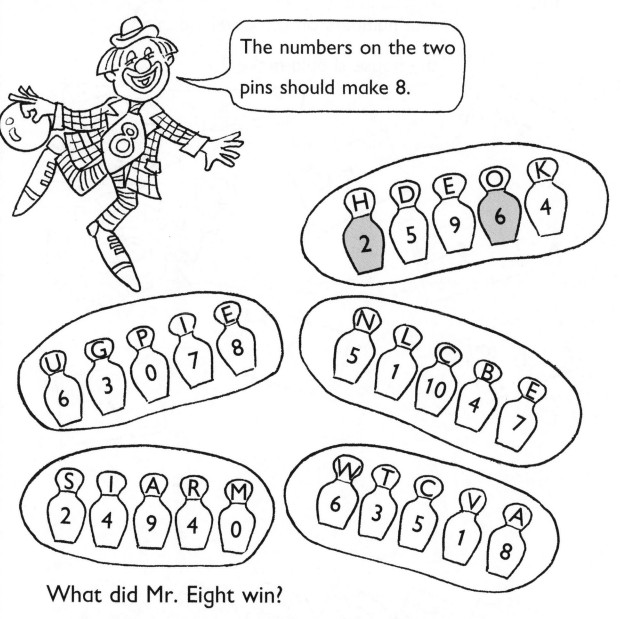

The numbers on the two pins should make 8.

What did Mr. Eight win?

Write the letters for the pins to find out.

EXERCISE 8

1. Where does Mr. Nine live?
    Match and write the letters in the houses below to find out.

The numbers on the envelope and the house should make 9.

8 I

5 C

4 S

6 C

2 R

7 U

4	1	7	3	2	5
C					

EXERCISE 9

1. Join each pair of Mr. Ten's socks.

The numbers on each pair should make 10.

EXERCISE 10

1. Divide each set into two parts.

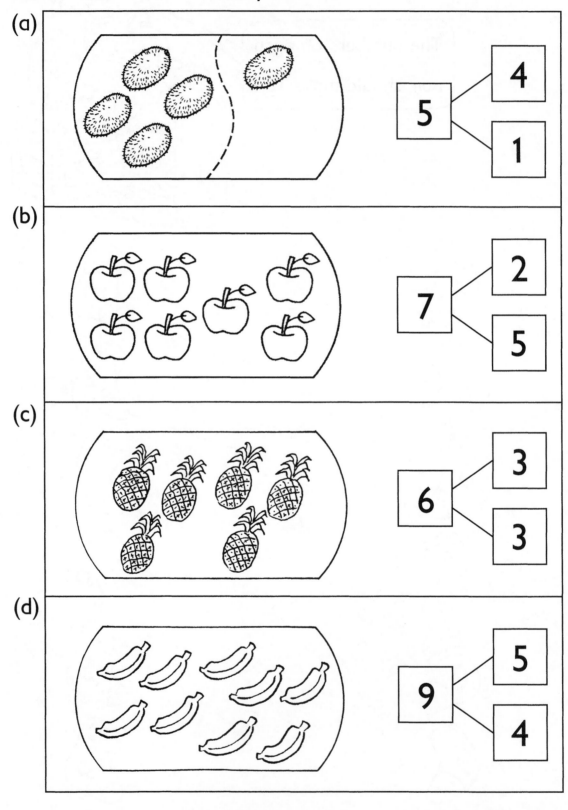

2. Write the missing numbers.

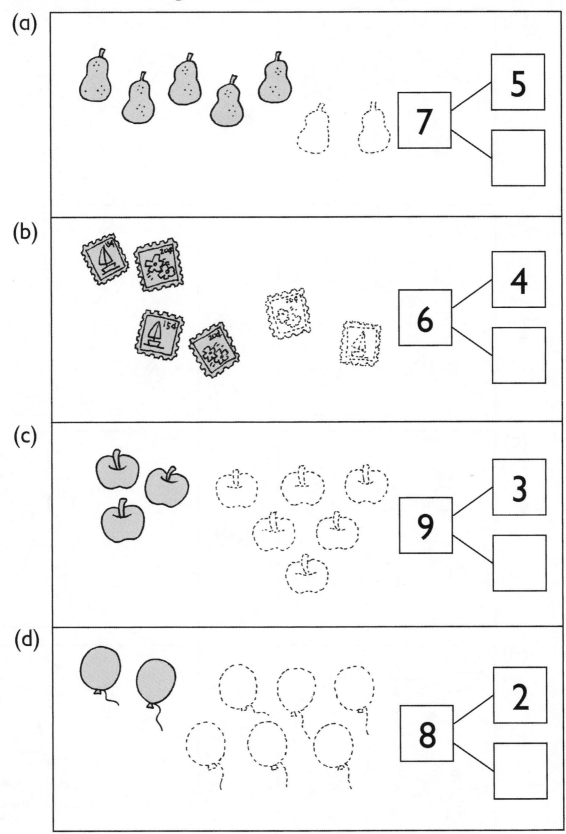

(a)

7 — 5, ☐

(b)

6 — 4, ☐

(c)

9 — 3, ☐

(d)

8 — 2, ☐

3. Draw the missing part.

(a)

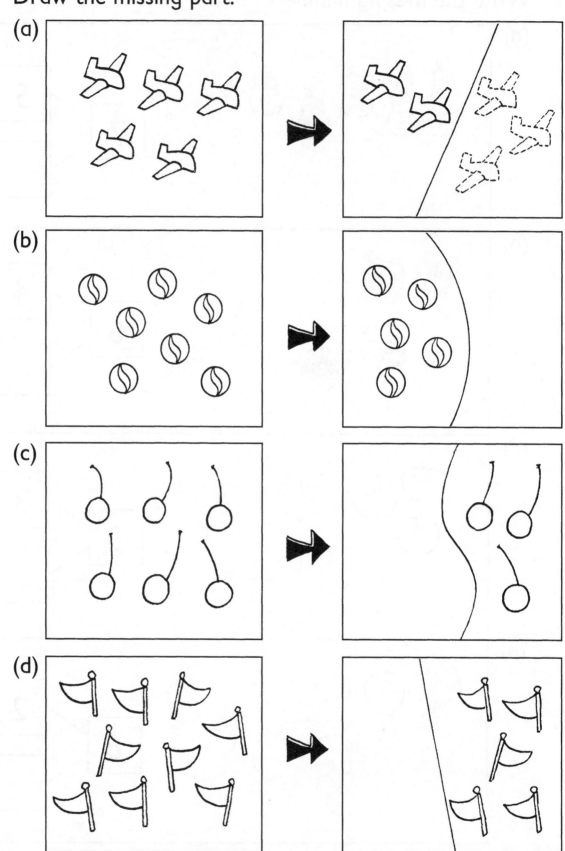

(b)

(c)

(d)

EXERCISE 11

1. Write the missing numbers.

(a)

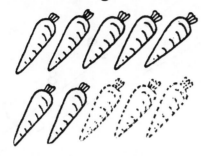

(b)

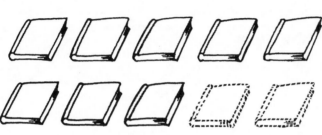

2. Write the missing numbers.

(a)

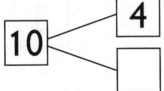

(b)

(c)

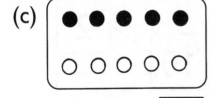

(d)

3. Join each pair of numbers that make 10.

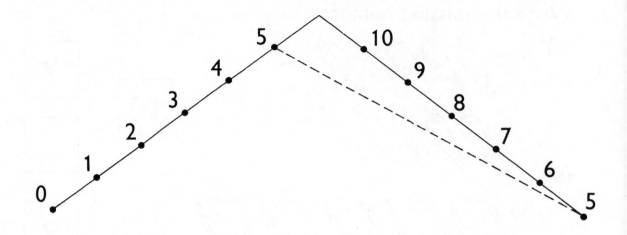

4. Write the missing numbers.

(a)

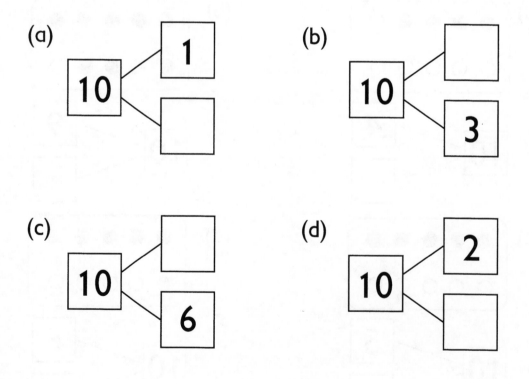

(b)

(c)

(d)

EXERCISE 12

1. Fill in the blanks.

(a)

There are _____ big boxes.

There are _____ small boxes.

There are _____ boxes altogether.

(b)

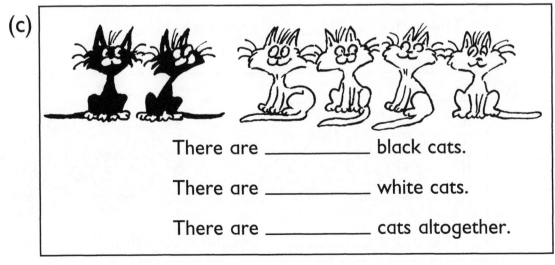

There are _____ boys.

There are _____ girls.

There are _____ children altogether.

(c)

There are _____ black cats.

There are _____ white cats.

There are _____ cats altogether.

2. Fill in the blanks.

(a)

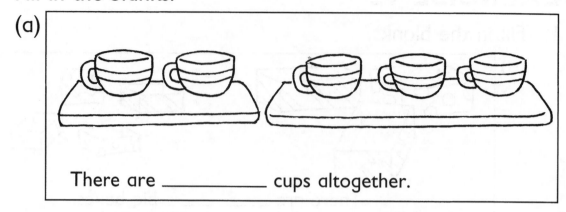

There are _____ cups altogether.

(b)

There are _____ fish altogether.

(c)

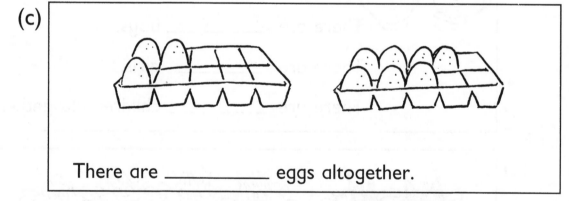

There are _____ eggs altogether.

(d)

There are _____ people altogether.

EXERCISE 13

1. Fill in the blanks.

(a)
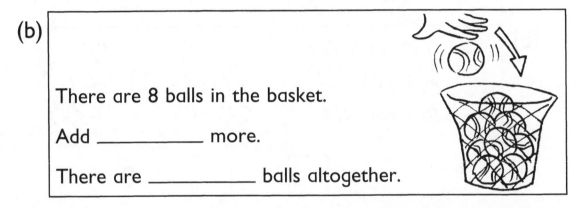

There are 3 flowers in the vase.

Add _____ more.

There are _____ flowers altogether.

(b)
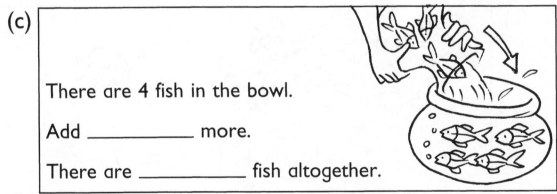

There are 8 balls in the basket.

Add _____ more.

There are _____ balls altogether.

(c)

There are 4 fish in the bowl.

Add _____ more.

There are _____ fish altogether.

(d)
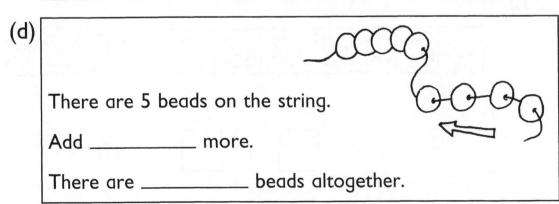

There are 5 beads on the string.

Add _____ more.

There are _____ beads altogether.

EXERCISE 14

1. Tell a story for each picture.
    Then complete the number sentence.

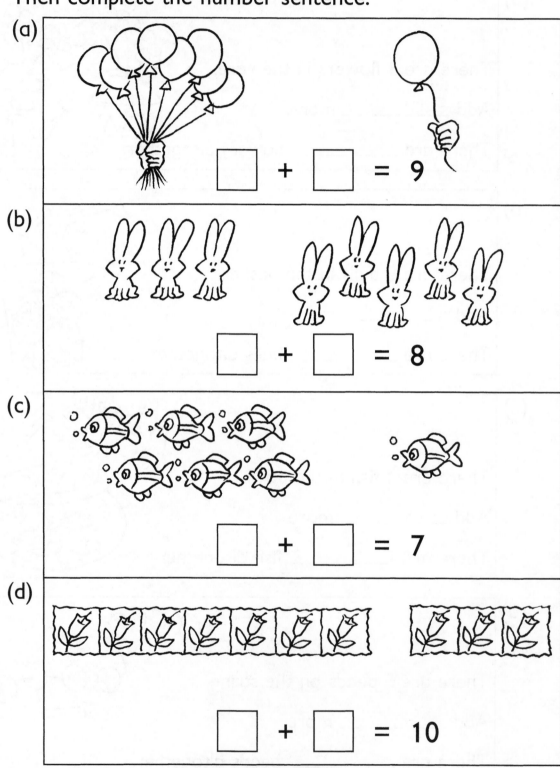

(a) ☐ + ☐ = 9

(b) ☐ + ☐ = 8

(c) ☐ + ☐ = 7

(d) ☐ + ☐ = 10

2. Tell two different stories for each picture.
   Then complete the number sentences.

(a)

☐ + ☐ = 8

☐ + ☐ = 8

(b)

☐ + ☐ = 6

☐ + ☐ = 6

3. Write an addition sentence for each picture.

(a)

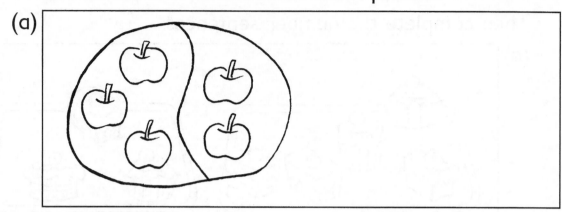

(b)

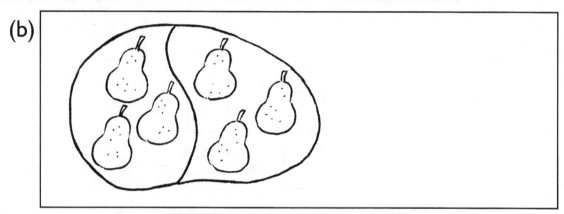

(c)

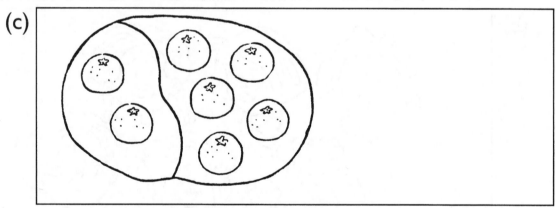

(d)

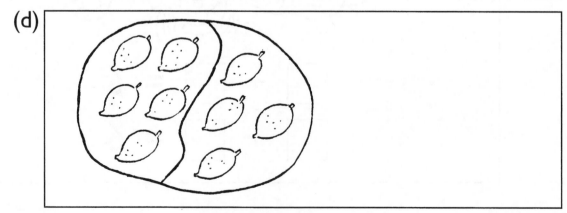

EXERCISE 15

1. Fill in the missing numbers.

(a)

6 + 2 = 8

8

6

2

(b)

1 + 5 = ☐

☐

1

5

(c)

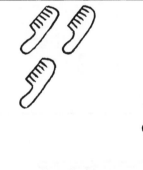

3 + 7 = ☐

☐

☐

☐

(d)

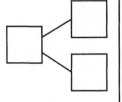

2 + 3 = ☐

☐

☐

☐

2. Add

4 + 5 =

4 + 3 =

4 + 2 =

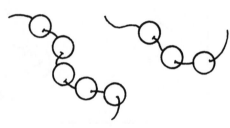

5 + 3 =

6 + 3 =

4 + 6 =

3. Color the flowers that match each big number.

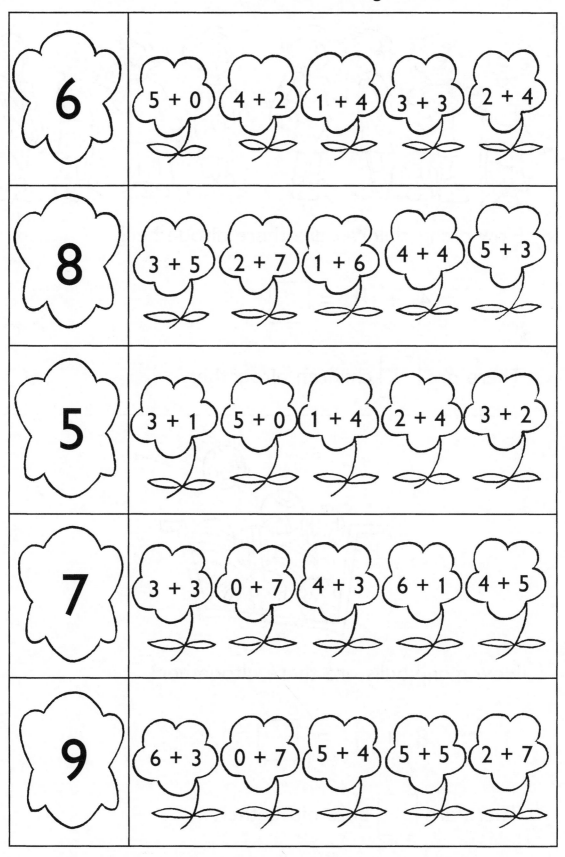

EXERCISE 16

1.

How many children are there altogether?

$$4 + 4 = \boxed{}$$

There are $\boxed{}$ children altogether.

2.

How many balls are there altogether?

$$8 + 1 = \boxed{}$$

There are $\boxed{}$ balls altogether.

3.

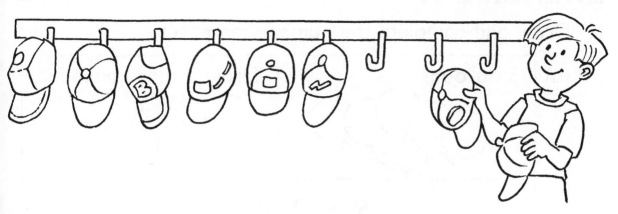

How many hats are there altogether?

$$6 + 2 = \boxed{}$$

There are $\boxed{}$ hats altogether.

4.

How many books are there on the shelf?

$$5 + 3 = \boxed{}$$

There are $\boxed{}$ books on the shelf.

EXERCISE 17

1. Draw and complete the number sentences.

(a) | 5 balloons | Draw 2 more balloons.

5 + 2 =

(b) | 4 birds | Draw 3 more birds.

4 + 3 =

(c) | 3 umbrellas | Draw 1 more umbrella.

3 + 1 =

(d) | 5 lollipops | Draw 2 more lollipops.

5 + 2 =

2.

There are 7 flowers in the vase.

Add 2 more.

$$7 + 2 = \boxed{}$$

There will be $\boxed{}$ flowers in the vase.

3.

There are 6 oranges in the bowl.

Add 4 more.

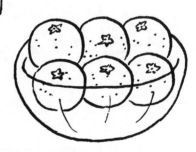

$$6 + 4 = \boxed{}$$

There will be $\boxed{}$ oranges in the bowl.

EXERCISE 18

1. Count on to add.

(a)
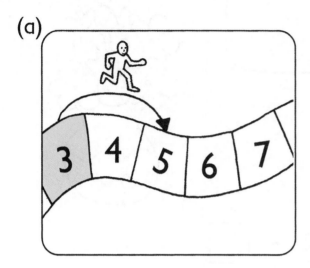

$$3 + 2 = \boxed{}$$

(b)

$$8 + 1 = \boxed{}$$

(c)

$$4 + 2 = \boxed{}$$

(d)

$$7 + 3 = \boxed{}$$

2. Add 1 to each number.

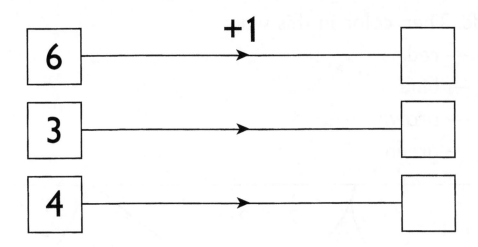

3. Add 2 to each number.

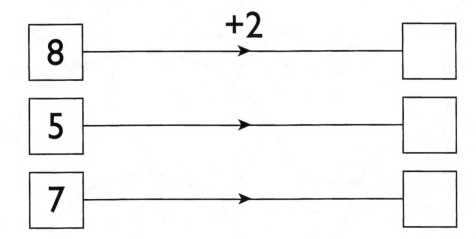

4. Add 3 to each number.

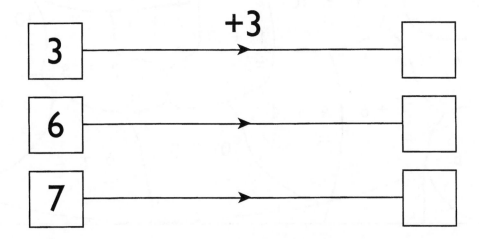

EXERCISE 19

1. Add. Then color in this way:

    10 — red
    9 — blue
    8 — brown
    7 — green

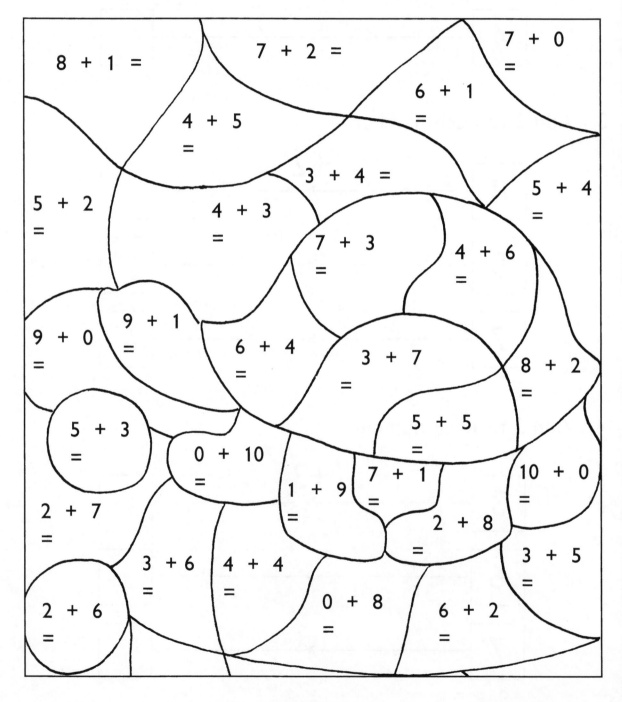

EXERCISE 20

1. Fill in the blanks.

(a)

There are 5 helicopters.

_____ fly away.

_____ helicopters are left.

(b)

There are 6 children.

_____ walk away.

_____ children are left.

(c)

There are 7 boxes.

I take away _____ .

_____ boxes are left.

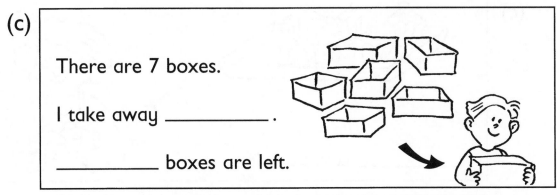

(d)

There are 9 beads.

I take away _____ .

_____ beads are left.

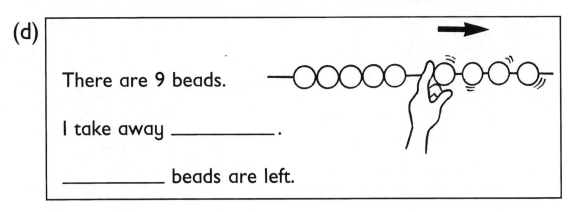

2. Fill in the blanks.

(a)

_____ fish are left.

(b)

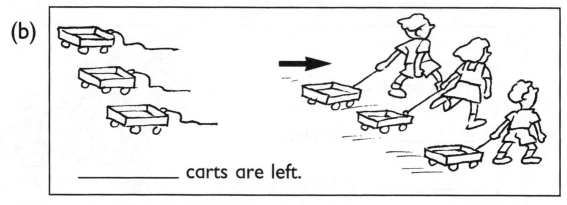

_____ carts are left.

(c)

_____ cakes are left.

(d)

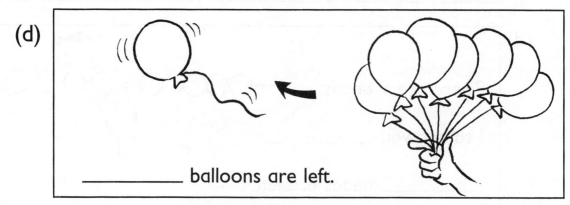

_____ balloons are left.

EXERCISE 21

1. Fill in the blanks.

(a)

There are 6 children.

4 of them are boys.

There are _____ girls.

(b)

There are 6 fish altogether.

There are 2 big fish.

There are _____ small fish.

(c)

There are 8 fruits.

5 of them are apples.

There are _____ pears.

(d)

There are 5 balls.

2 of them are grey.

The rest are white.

There are _____ white balls.

2. Fill in the blanks.

(a)

There are 8 trees altogether.

4 of them are cut down.

_____ trees are left.

(b)

I bought 7 oranges.

I ate 2 of them.

_____ oranges are left.

(c)

There are 6 fruits altogether.

2 of them are papayas.

The rest are pineapples.

There are _____ pineapples.

(d)

There are 5 children.

3 of them are

swimming.

_____ are not swimming.

EXERCISE 22

1. Tell a story for each picture.

    Then complete the number sentence.

(a)

☐ − ☐ = 4

(b)

☐ − ☐ = 4

(c)

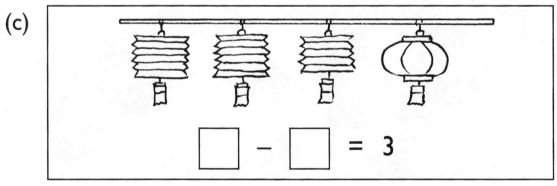

☐ − ☐ = 3

(d)

☐ − ☐ = 5

2. Tell two different stories for each picture.

   Then complete the number sentences.

(a)

$$\boxed{} - \boxed{} = 2$$

$$\boxed{} - \boxed{} = 5$$

(b)

$$\boxed{} - \boxed{} = 1$$

$$\boxed{} - \boxed{} = 4$$

3. Write two subtraction sentences for each picture.

(a)

(b)

(c)

(d)

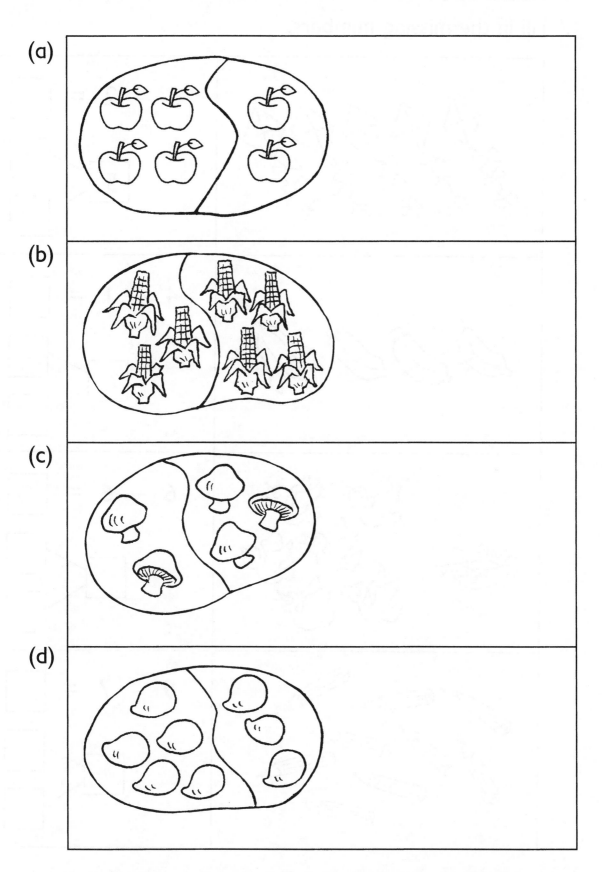

EXERCISE 23

1. Fill in the missing numbers.

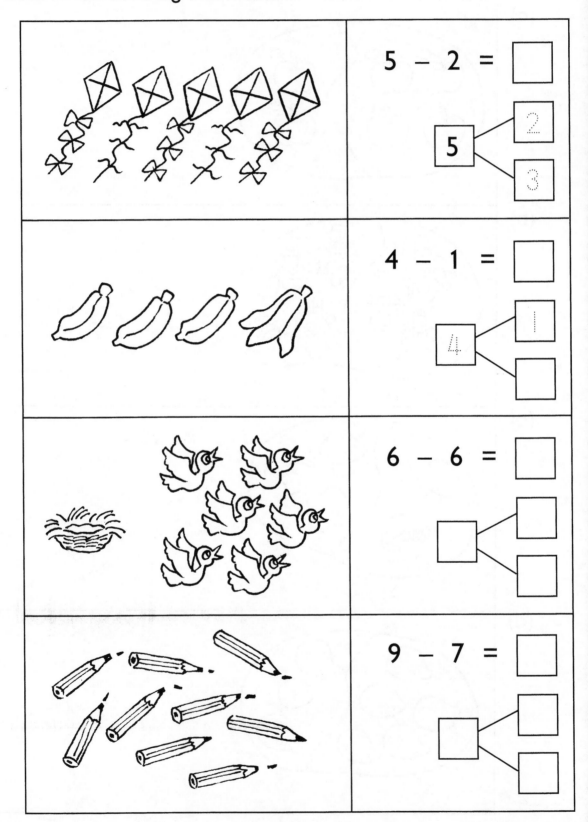

$5 - 2 = \boxed{}$

$5 \begin{cases} \boxed{2} \\ \boxed{3} \end{cases}$

$4 - 1 = \boxed{}$

$4 \begin{cases} \boxed{1} \\ \boxed{} \end{cases}$

$6 - 6 = \boxed{}$

$9 - 7 = \boxed{}$

2. Subtract.

8 − 4 =

7 − 4 =

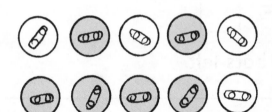

10 − 4 =

6 − 3 =

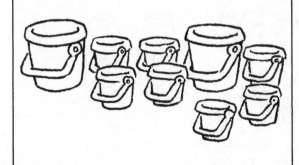

9 − 2 =

8 − 2 =

EXERCISE 24

1.

There are 7 bats
in the box.
Take away 2 bats.

7 – 2 = ☐

There will be ☐ bats left.

2.

I have 6 bottles of milk.
I give away 4 bottles.

6 – 4 = ☐

There are ☐ bottles left.

3.

There are 8 hats.

3 are big hats.

The rest are small hats.

$$8 - 3 = \boxed{}$$

There are $\boxed{}$ small hats.

4.

I buy 10 cup cakes.

I put 4 of them on a plate.

The rest are in the box.

 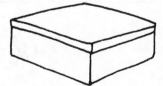

$$10 - 4 = \boxed{}$$

There are $\boxed{}$ cup cakes in the box.

EXERCISE 25

1. Complete the number sentences.

(a)

5 + 1 = ☐   1 + 5 = ☐

6 − 5 = ☐   6 − 1 = ☐

(b)

4 + 3 = ☐   3 + 4 = ☐

7 − 4 = ☐   7 − 3 = ☐

(c)

3 + 2 = ☐   2 + 3 = ☐

5 − 2 = ☐   5 − 3 = ☐

2. Write two addition sentences and two subtraction sentences for each picture.

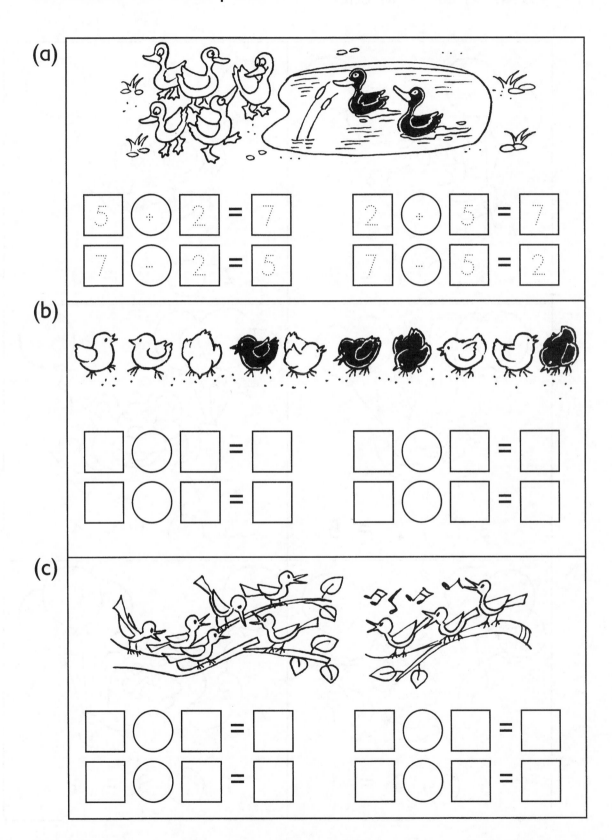

(a)

$$5 \; \boxed{+} \; 2 = 7 \qquad 2 \; \boxed{+} \; 5 = 7$$

$$7 \; \boxed{-} \; 2 = 5 \qquad 7 \; \boxed{-} \; 5 = 2$$

(b)

$$\square \bigcirc \square = \square \qquad \square \bigcirc \square = \square$$

$$\square \bigcirc \square = \square \qquad \square \bigcirc \square = \square$$

(c)

$$\square \bigcirc \square = \square \qquad \square \bigcirc \square = \square$$

$$\square \bigcirc \square = \square \qquad \square \bigcirc \square = \square$$

EXERCISE 26

1. Write '+' or '−' in each ◯.

3 ◯ 1 = 2

2 ◯ 2 = 0

3 ◯ 2 = 5

5 ◯ 1 = 4

4 ◯ 3 = 1

1 ◯ 3 = 4

2. Use the numbers and signs in each box to write a number sentence.

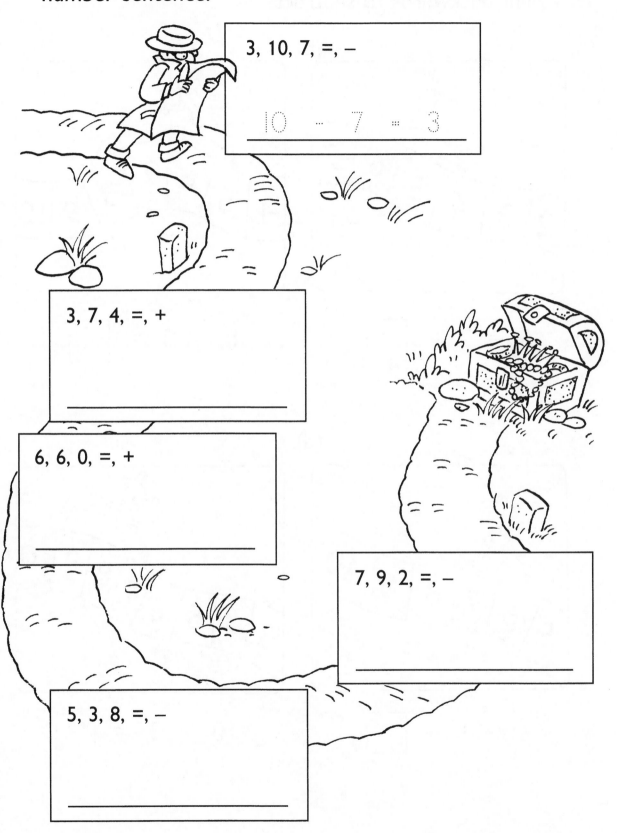

3, 10, 7, =, −

10 − 7 = 3

3, 7, 4, =, +

_____

6, 6, 0, =, +

_____

7, 9, 2, =, −

_____

5, 3, 8, =, −

_____

EXERCISE 27

1. Count backwards to subtract.

(a)

6 – 2 = ☐

(b)

8 – 3 = ☐

(c)

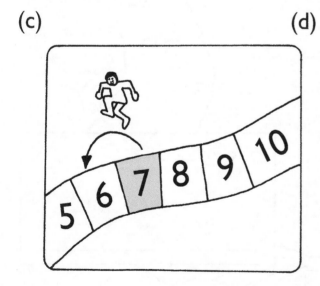

7 – 1 = ☐

(d)

10 – 3 = ☐

2. Subtract 1 from each number.

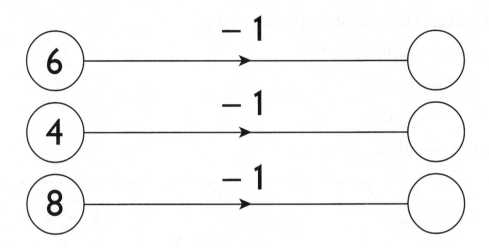

3. Subtract 2 from each number.

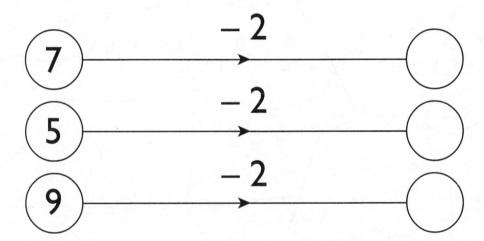

4. Subtract 3 from each number.

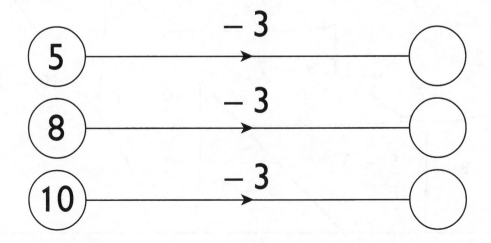

EXERCISE 28

1. Subtract. Then color in this way:

    0 — yellow

    1 — red

    2 — green

    Others — blue

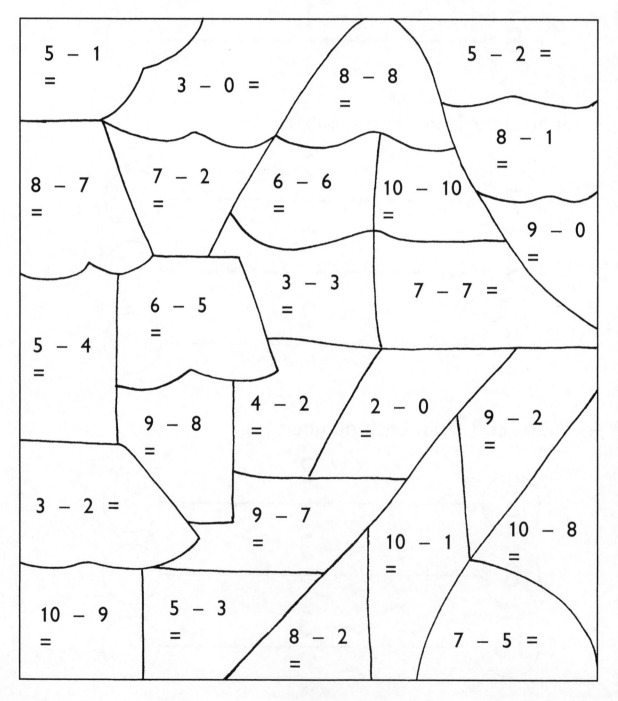

EXERCISE 29

1. Cross out the ducks that do not belong to the house.

EXERCISE 30

1.

How many ducks are there altogether?

4 ◯ 3 = ☐

There are ☐ ducks altogether.

2.

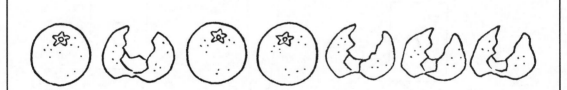

How many oranges are left?

7 ◯ 4 = ☐

☐ oranges are left.

3.

How many children are there altogether?

7 ◯ 3 = ☐

There are ☐ children altogether.

4.

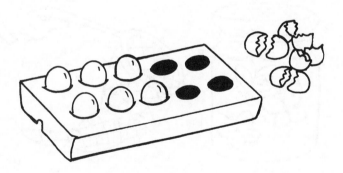

How many eggs are used?

10 ◯ 6 = ☐

☐ eggs are used.

5.

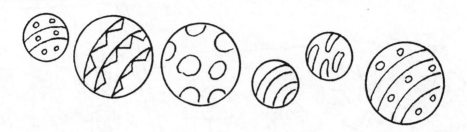

How many small balls are there?

6 ◯ 3 = ☐

There are ☐ small balls.

6.

How many butterflies are there altogether?

3 ◯ 1 = ☐

There are ☐ butterflies altogether.

EXERCISE 31

1.

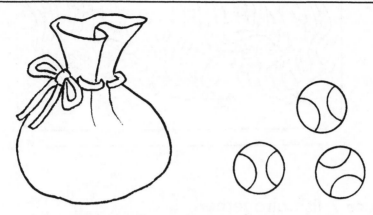

There are 4 balls in the bag.

How many balls are there altogether?

4 ◯ ☐ = ☐

There are ☐ balls altogether.

2.

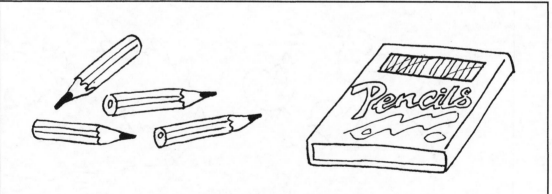

There are 10 pencils altogether.

How many pencils are there in the box?

10 ◯ ☐ = ☐

There are ☐ pencils in the box.

3.

There are 7 fish altogether.

How many fish are hidden?

7 ⃝ ▢ = ▢

▢ fish are hidden.

4.

2 chicks are hidden in the bush.

How many chicks are there altogether?

2 ⃝ ▢ = ▢

There are ▢ chicks altogether.

5.

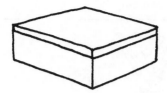 

There are 4 cakes in the box.

How many cakes are there altogether?

4 ◯ ▢ = ▢

There are ▢ cakes altogether.

6.

There are 8 apples altogether.

How many apples are there in the bag?

8 ◯ ▢ = ▢

There are ▢ apples in the bag.

EXERCISE 32

1. Match.

(a)

2nd   3rd   1st

(b)

I am 5th.

I am 1st.

6th   2nd   4th

(c)

4th   1st   3rd

2. (a) Color the 3rd glass.

1st

(b) Color 3 flags.

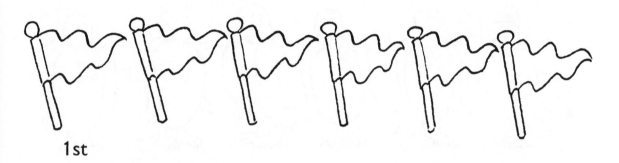

1st

3. (a) Color the 5th fan.

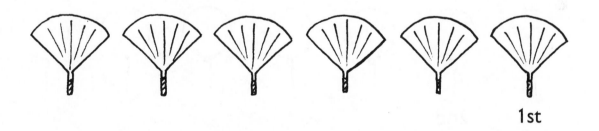

1st

(b) Color 5 butterflies.

1st

EXERCISE 33

1. Draw an apple on the 6th plate.

1st

2. Draw a hat on the 2nd penguin.

6th

3. Draw a star on the 5th balloon.

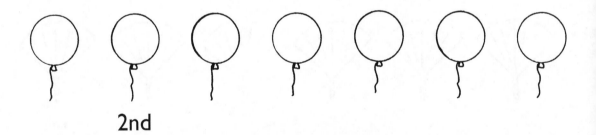

2nd

4. Draw a flag on the 4th boat.

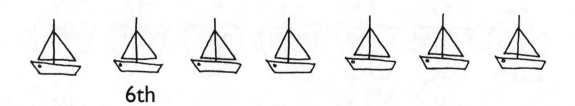

6th

EXERCISE 34

1. Color the 6th ball from the right.

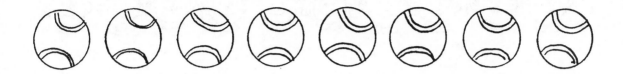

2. Color the 3rd tree from the left.

3. Color the 5th bell from the right.

4. Color the 2nd orange from the left.

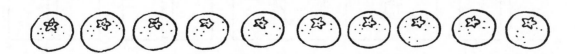

5. Draw a hat on the 4th child from the right.

6. Fill in **1st**, **2nd**, **3rd**, **4th** and **5th** to show the order.

(a)

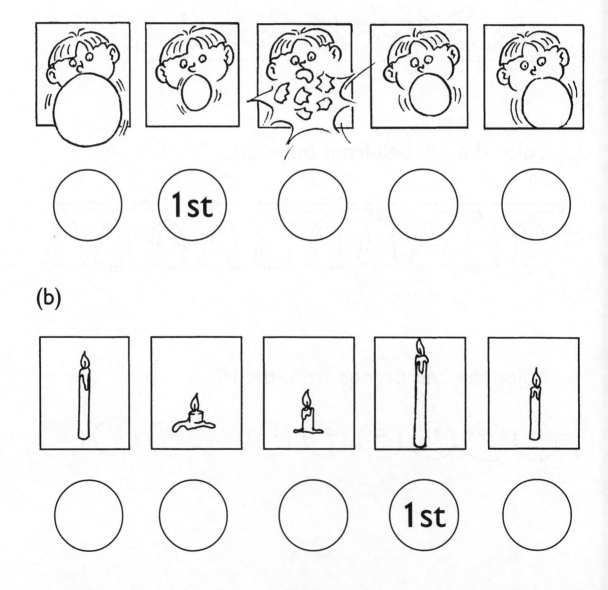

(b)

REVIEW 1

1. Write the numbers.

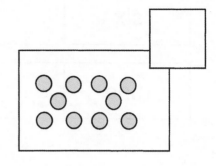

2. Count and write the numbers in words.

	Numbers in words
🍊🍊🍊🍊	
🐟🐟	
🥕🥕🥕🥕🥕	
🦋🦋🦋🦋🦋🦋🦋🦋🦋	
🦆🦆🦆	

3. Write the numbers.

six	

seven	

nine	

zero	

4. Write the numbers in words.

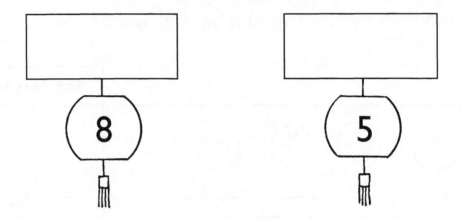

5. (a) Match the balloon to the 3rd child from the right.

   (b) Match the flower to the 4th child from the left.

   (c) Draw a hat on the 9th child from the right.

6. Write the missing numbers.

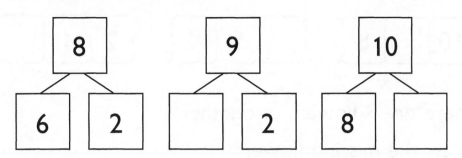

7. (a) Color the two numbers that make 8.

3   10   5   7

(b) Color the two numbers that make 10.

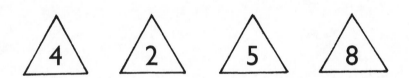

4   2   5   8

8. How many fruits are there altogether?

(a)   (b)

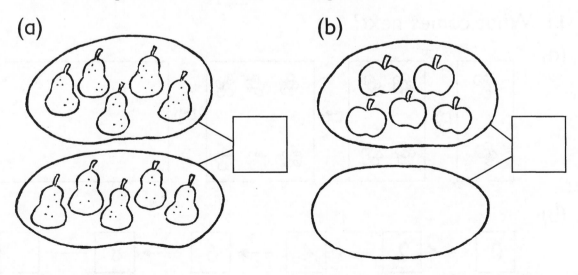

9. Fill in the missing numbers.

| 10 | | 8 |

| | 5 | 4 |

| 2 | 1 | |

10. There are **9** flowers altogether.

Draw the missing flowers.

11. What comes next?

(a)

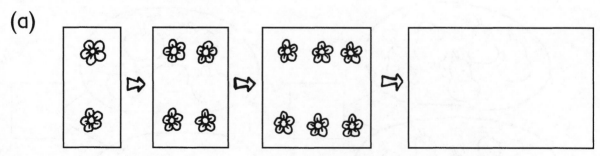

(b)

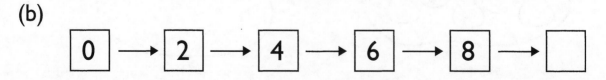

0 → 2 → 4 → 6 → 8 → ☐

REVIEW 2

1. Add or subtract.

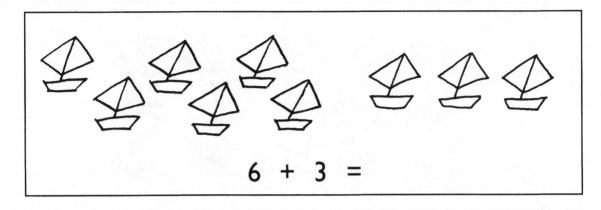

6 + 3 =

5 + 4 =

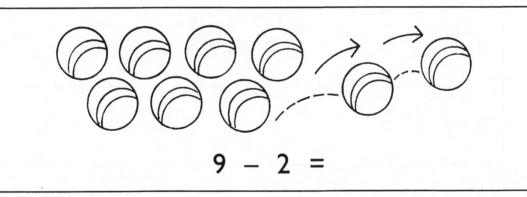

9 – 2 =

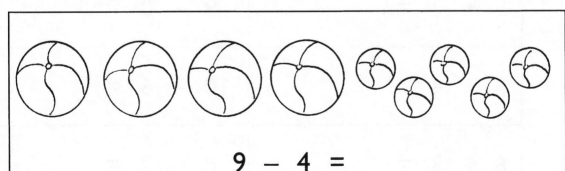

9 – 4 =

2. Write two addition sentences and two subtraction sentences for the picture.

3. Do these.

0 + 5 =	5 − 4 =
9 + 1 =	7 − 7 =
5 + 2 =	9 − 0 =
4 + 4 =	10 − 6 =
6 + 3 =	8 − 2 =

4.

How many eggs are there altogether?

$4 \bigcirc 5 = \square$

There are _____ eggs altogether.

5.

  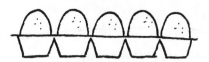

How many watermelons are taken away?

$7 \bigcirc 2 = \square$

_____ watermelons are taken away.

6.

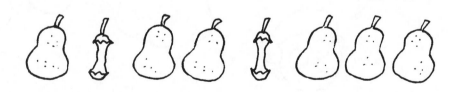

How many pears are left?

$8 \bigcirc 2 = \square$

_____ pears are left.

7. How many stamps does Nicole have left?

I have 8 stamps.

I give away 2 stamps.

Nicole

8 ◯ 2 = ☐

Nicole has _____ stamps left.

---

8. How many oranges are there altogether?

There are 3 oranges in the bag.

3 ◯ 4 = ☐

There are _____ oranges altogether.

REVIEW 3

1. Write the numbers.

   Then match the numbers and words.

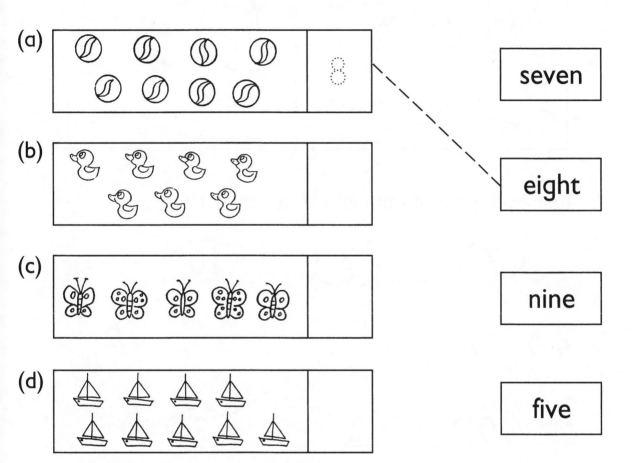

(a)   8

(b)

(c)

(d)

seven

eight

nine

five

2. Check the set that has **more**.

3. Check the set that has **less**.

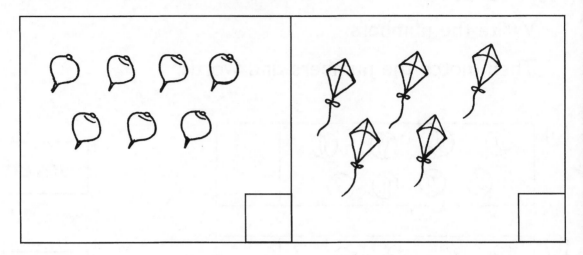

4. Join each pair of numbers that make 10.

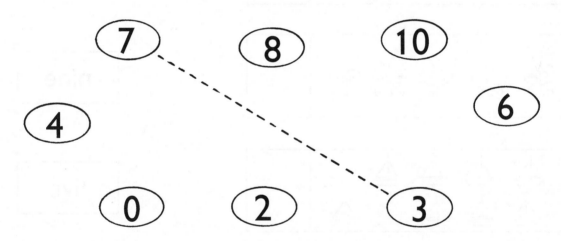

5. Fill in **1st**, **2nd**, **3rd**, **4th** and **5th** to show the order.

6. Add or subtract.

(a)

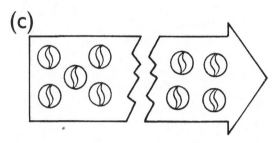

5 + 2 = _____

(b)

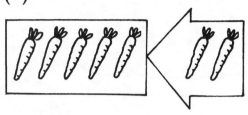

6 + 3 = _____

(c)

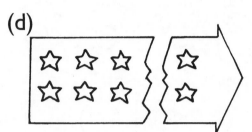

9 − 4 = _____

(d)

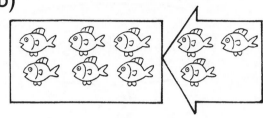

8 − 2 = _____

(e)

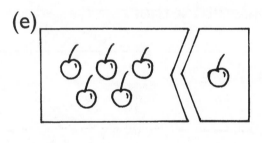

5 + 1 = _____

(f)

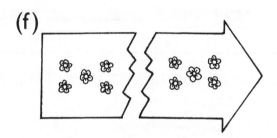

10 − 5 = _____

7. Write + or − in each ◯.

(a) 8 ◯ 7 = 1

(b) 3 ◯ 7 = 10

(c) 6 ◯ 3 = 9

(d) 9 ◯ 9 = 0

(e) 10 ◯ 2 = 8

(f) 7 ◯ 2 = 9

(g) 5 ◯ 1 = 4

(h) 10 ◯ 8 = 2

8. How many buttons do they have altogether?

I have 6 buttons.

I have 2 buttons.

Sally

Jane

□ ○ □ = □

They have _____ buttons altogether.

---

9. How many marbles does Ali have?

I have 4 marbles.

We have 9 marbles altogether.

Peter

Ali

□ ○ □ = □

Ali has _____ marbles.

EXERCISE 35

1. Match.

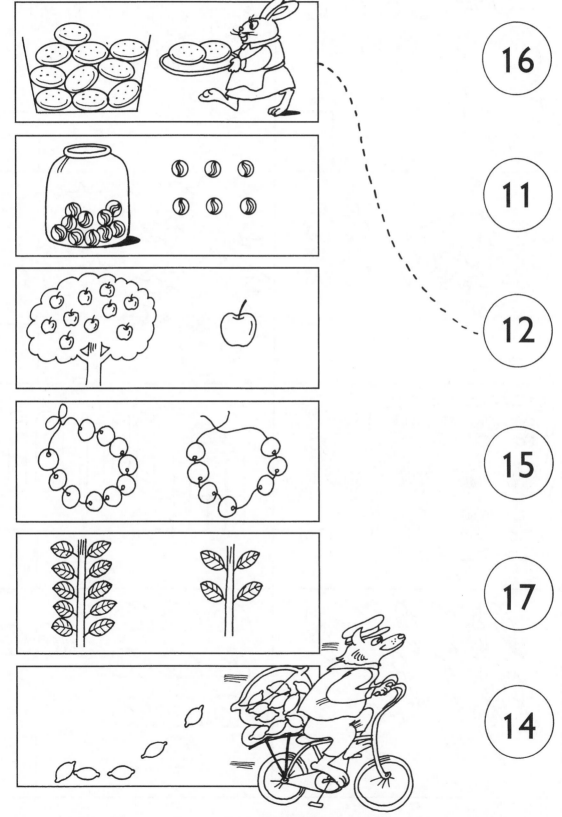

2. Write the numbers.

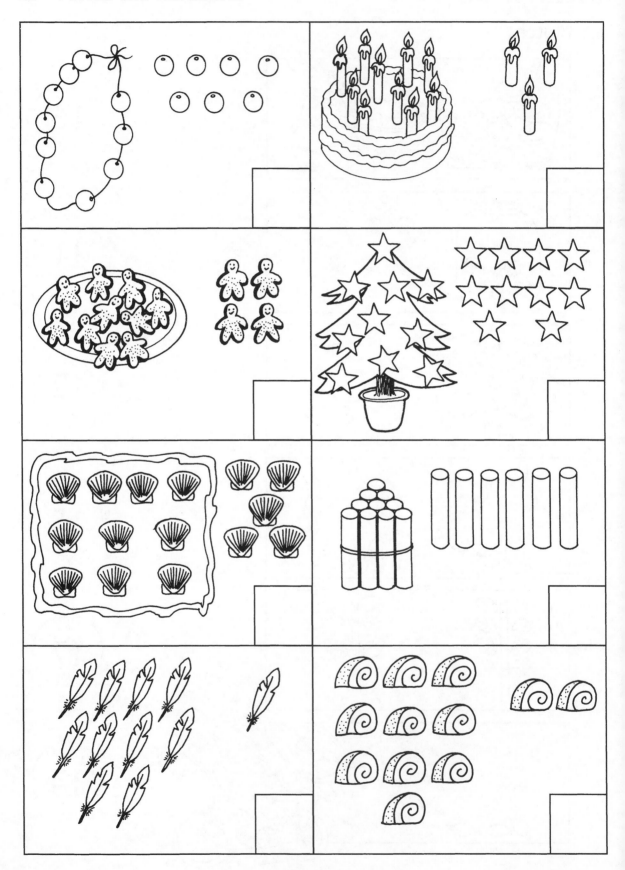

3. Circle a set of 10 fish.

   Then write the number.

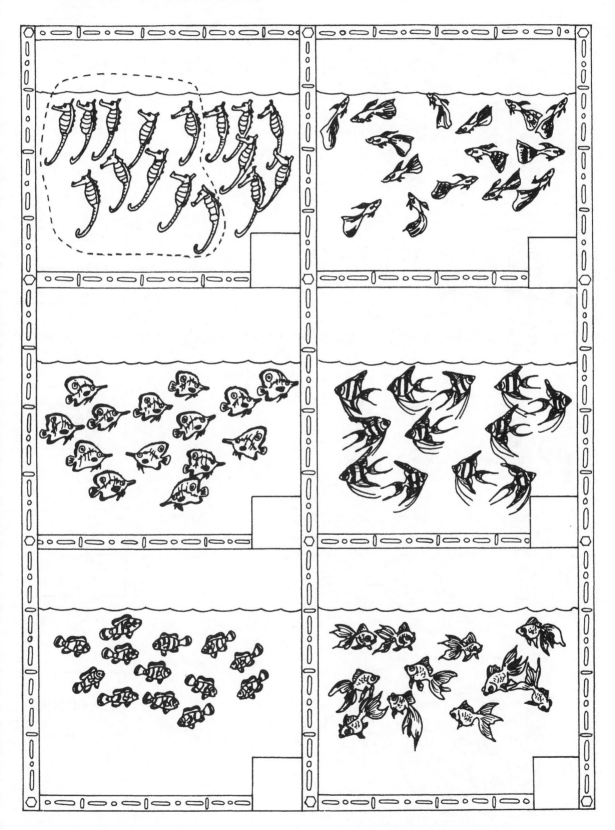

EXERCISE 36

1. Write the numbers.
   Then match.

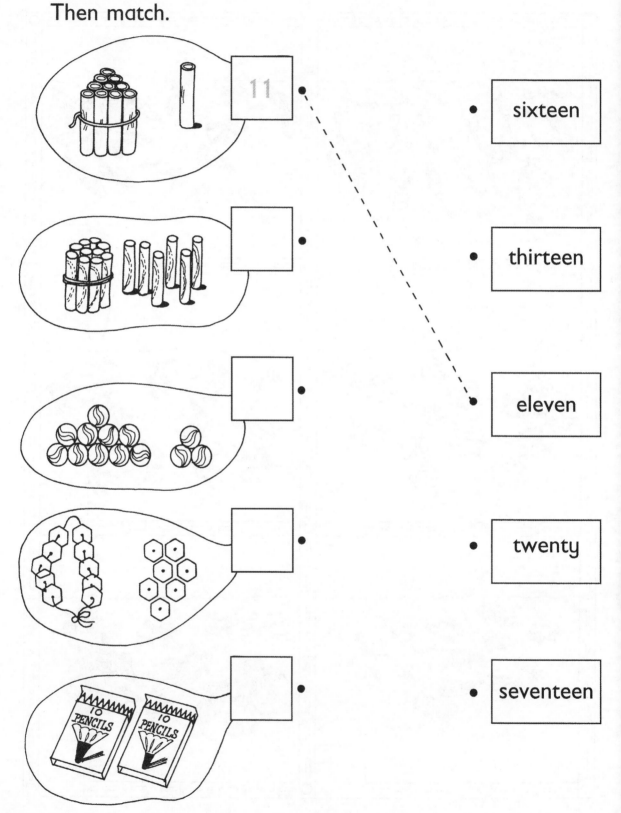

11

sixteen

thirteen

eleven

twenty

seventeen

2. Write the numbers.

sixteen

thirteen

eleven

twelve

twenty

seventeen

fourteen

nineteen

eighteen

fifteen

EXERCISE 37

1. Fill in the missing numbers.

(a)

10 and 6 make _____.

(b)

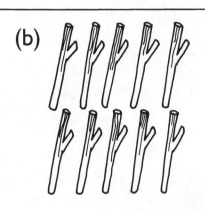 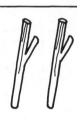

10 and 2 make _____.

(c)

10 and 9 make _____.

(d)

10 and 5 make _____.

2. Complete the number sentences.

(a)

$$10 + 4 =$$

(b)

$$10 + 8 =$$

(c)

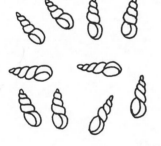

$$10 + 3 =$$

(d)

$$10 + 7 =$$

EXERCISE 38

1. Join the dots in order from 1 to 20.

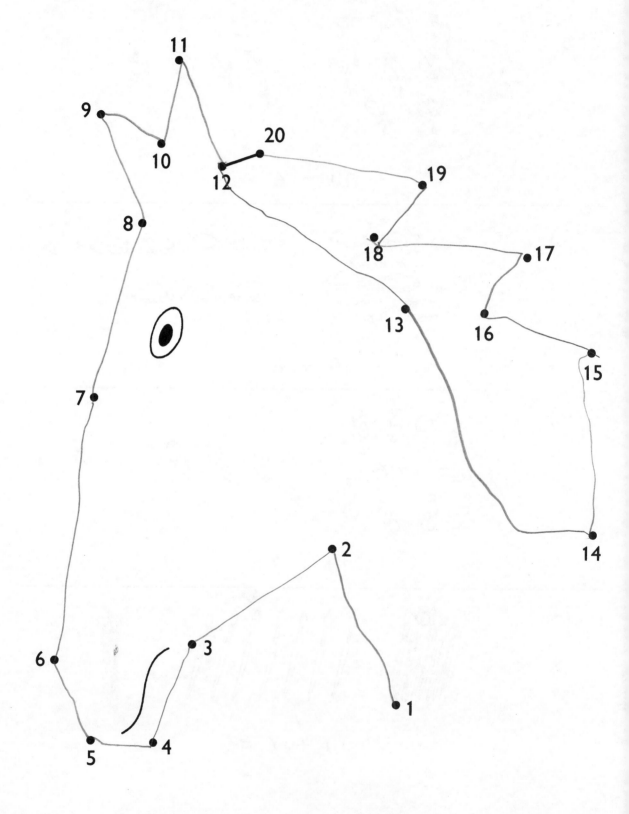

2. Fill in the missing numbers.

(a)

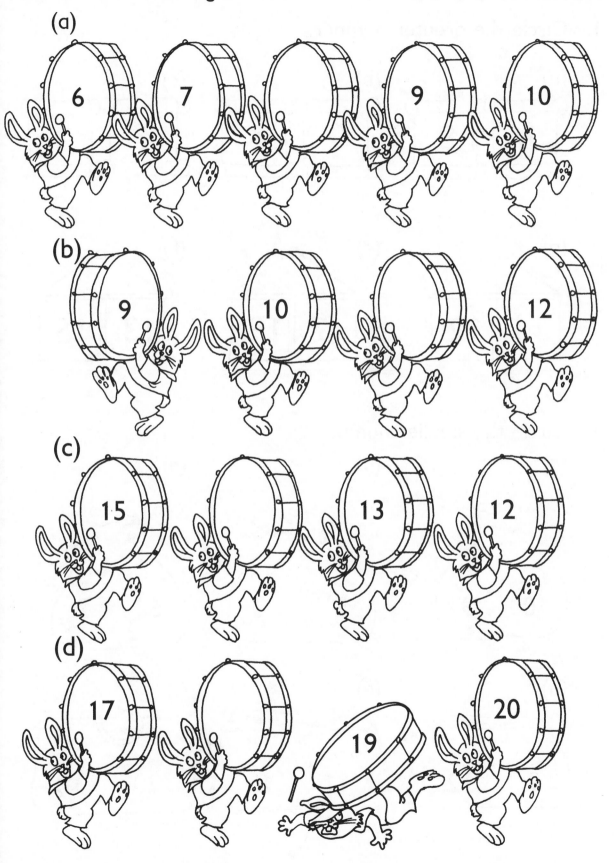

6 7 ___ 9 10

(b)

9 10 ___ 12

(c)

15 ___ 13 12

(d)

17 ___ 19 20

EXERCISE 39

1. Circle the greater number.

(a)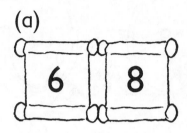

(b)

(c)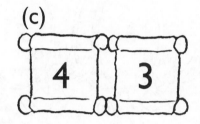

(d)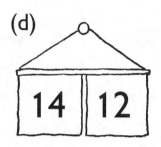

(e)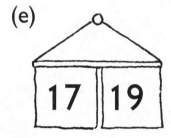

(f)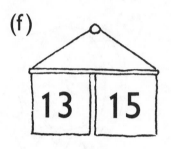

2. Circle the smaller number.

(a)

(b)

(c)

(d)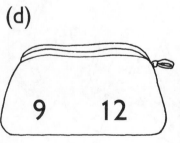

(e)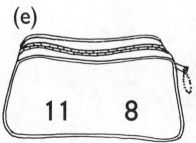

(f)

3. Circle the greatest number.

(a)

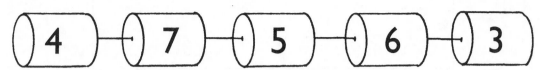

4 — 7 — 5 — 6 — 3

(b)

| 15 | 18 | 17 | 14 | 16 | 12 |

4. Circle the smallest number.

(a)

6   10   8   7   9

(b)

16   14   19   20   18

(c)

14 18 16 12 9 10

5. Write the numbers in order. Begin with the given number.

(a)
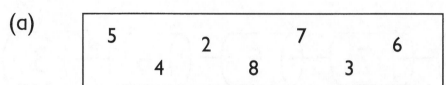

5		7		6
	2			
4		8	3	

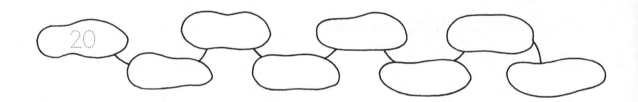

(b)
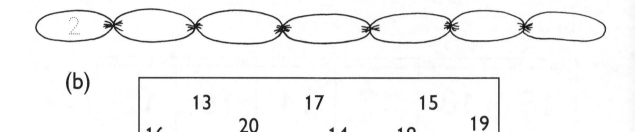

| | 13 | | 17 | | 15 | |
| 16 | | 20 | | 14 | 18 | 19 |

6. Arrange these numbers in order.
(a) Begin with the smallest number.

_____ _____ _____ _____ _____

13   20
15   12
10

(b) Begin with the greatest number.

9   18

15   11   14

_____ _____ _____ _____ _____

EXERCISE 40

1. Add.

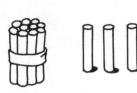 

10 + 3 =

 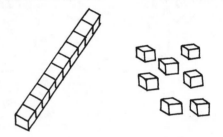

8 + 10 =

6 + 10 =

10 + 7 =

10 + 2 =

10 + 5 =

4 + 10 =

1 + 10 =

2. Add.

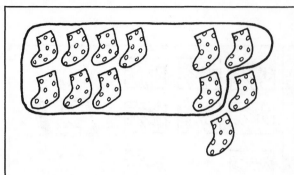

7 + 5 =

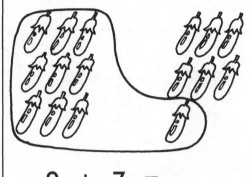

9 + 7 =

4 + 9 =

8 + 5 =

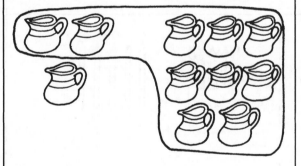

3 + 8 =

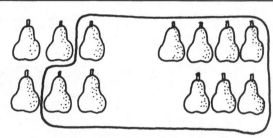

6 + 7 =

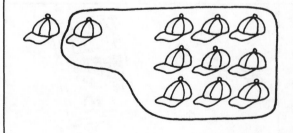

2 + 9 =

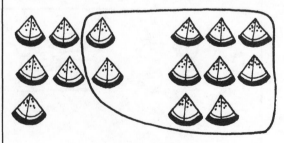

7 + 8 =

EXERCISE 41

1. Add.

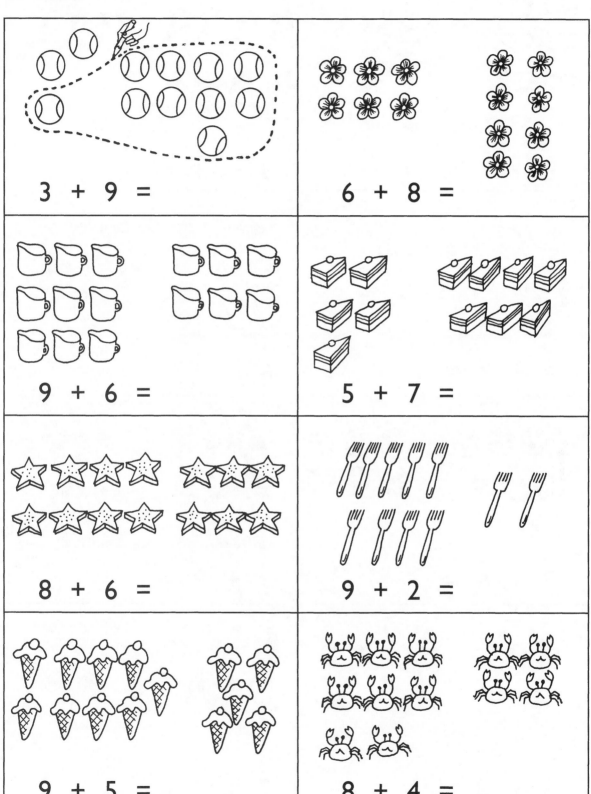

3 + 9 =

6 + 8 =

9 + 6 =

5 + 7 =

8 + 6 =

9 + 2 =

9 + 5 =

8 + 4 =

2. Add.

  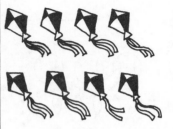

6 + 7 =   8 + 3 =

4 + 7 =   6 + 9 =

 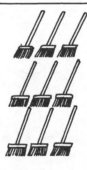

7 + 6 =   9 + 9 =

 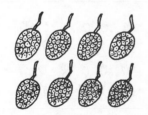 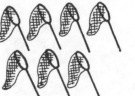

3 + 8 =   7 + 4 =

98

EXERCISE 42

1. Add.

12 + 3 =

16 + 3 =

5 + 12 =

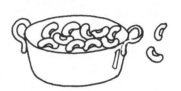

12 + 6 =

4 + 15 =

15 + 3 =

17 + 3 =

8 + 11 =

2. Add.

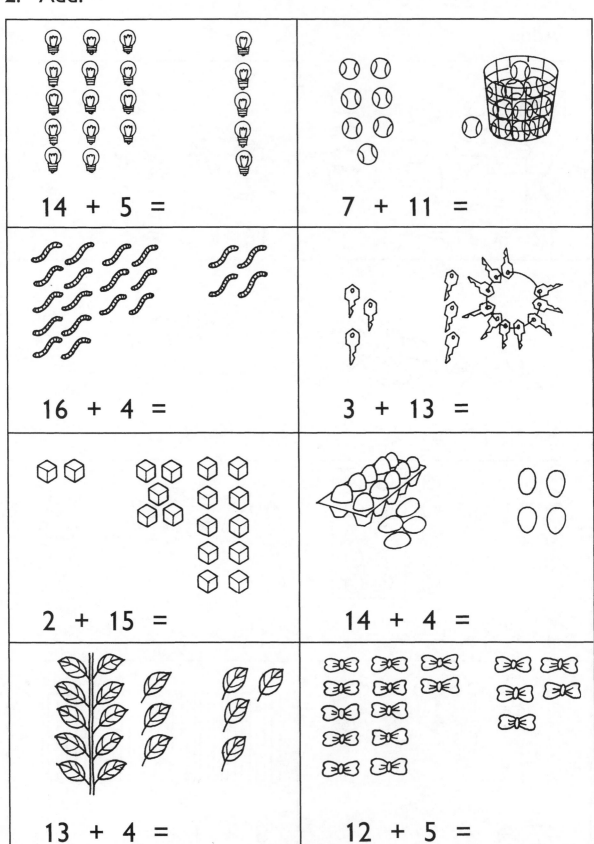

14 + 5 =

7 + 11 =

16 + 4 =

3 + 13 =

2 + 15 =

14 + 4 =

13 + 4 =

12 + 5 =

3. Complete the addition sentence for each picture.

10 + 10 =   11 +   =

12 +   =   10 +   =

11 +   =   10 +   =

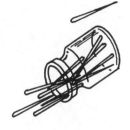  

14 +   =   13 +   =

EXERCISE 43

1. Subtract.

15 – 3 =

14 – 4 =

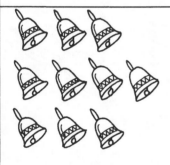 

19 – 6 =

 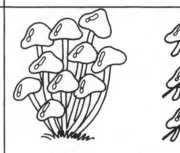 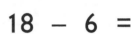

18 – 6 =

16 – 6 =

17 – 4 =

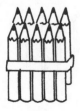 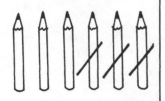

16 – 3 =

19 – 5 =

2. Subtract.

13 − 1 =   16 − 5 =

 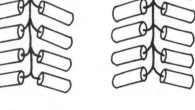

17 − 5 =   20 − 3 =

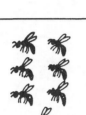 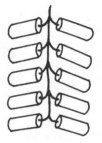

19 − 7 =   15 − 4 =

 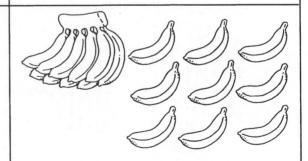

18 − 5 =   19 − 4 =

3. Complete the subtraction sentence for each picture.

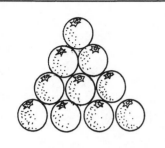 

14 – 3 =

17 – =

12 – =

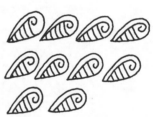

17 – =

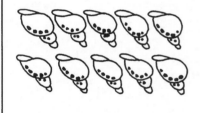

13 – =

14 – =

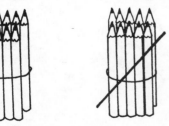

20 – =

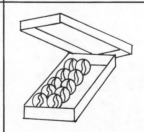

16 – =

EXERCISE 44

1. Subtract.

15 – 10 =

10 – 4 =

10 – 6 =

12 – 10 =

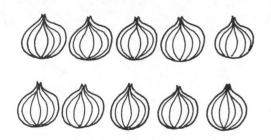

10 – 5 =

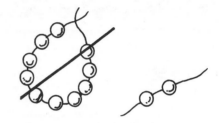

17 – 10 =

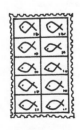

20 – 10 =

10 – 8 =

2. Subtract.

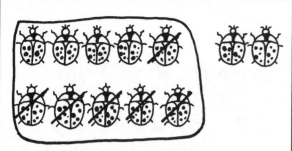

12 – 6 =

11 – 6 =

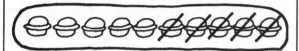

13 – 5 =

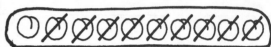

11 – 9 =

12 – 8 =

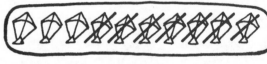

15 – 7 =

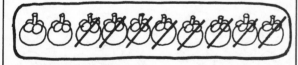

14 – 8 =

16 – 9 =

3. Subtract.

17 − 8 =

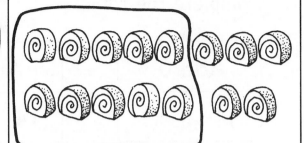

15 − 8 =

13 − 6 =

18 − 9 =

11 − 3 =

14 − 6 =

12 − 5 =

16 − 7 =

EXERCISE 45

1. Complete the tables.

Add 0	
11	
13	
20	
14	
19	
12	

Add 1	
14	
17	
13	
19	
15	
18	

Add 2	
12	
16	
10	
18	
14	
11	

Subtract 0	
15	
19	
11	
17	
13	
10	

Subtract 1	
17	
14	
20	
15	
18	
12	

Subtract 2	
10	
19	
16	
11	
20	
13	

2. Fill in the missing numbers.

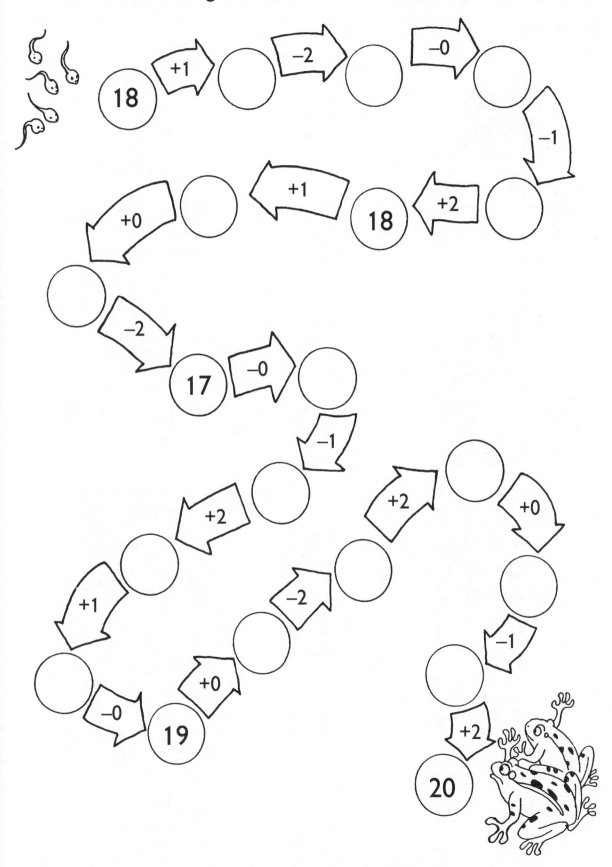

EXERCISE 46

1. Match.

2. Add or subtract.

14
9 + 5

7 + 4

15 − 9

16 − 8

5 + 7

12 − 6

11 − 3

13 − 7

9 + 3

14 − 5

4 + 8

8 + 5

EXERCISE 47

1. Add or subtract.

    Then color the spaces with the answer 16.

    You will find a path to bring Miss Ladybird home.

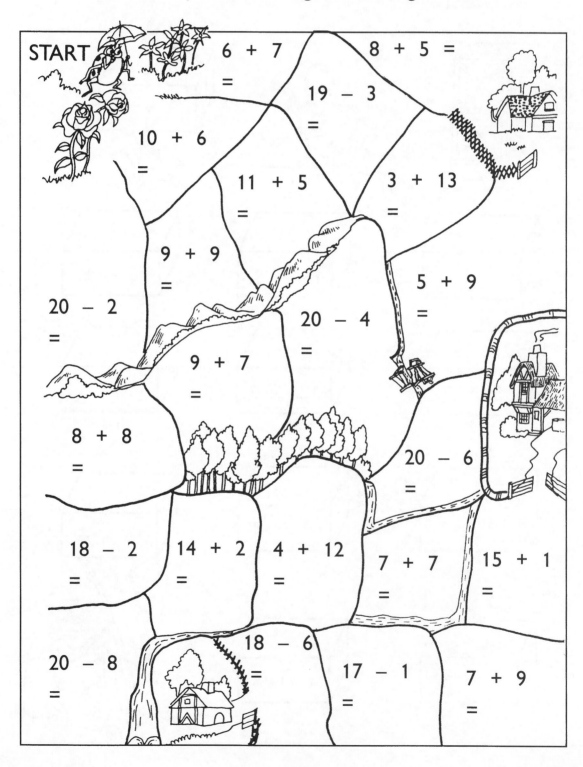

START

6 + 7 =

8 + 5 =

19 – 3 =

10 + 6 =

11 + 5 =

3 + 13 =

9 + 9 =

5 + 9 =

20 – 2 =

20 – 4 =

9 + 7 =

8 + 8 =

20 – 6 =

18 – 2 =

14 + 2 =

4 + 12 =

7 + 7 =

15 + 1 =

20 – 8 =

18 – 6 =

17 – 1 =

7 + 9 =

EXERCISE 48

1. Write '+' or '−' in each ◯.

    10 ◯ 4 = 6   10 ◯ 4 = 14

    9 ◯ 9 = 18   8 ◯ 8 = 0

    9 ◯ 6 = 15   7 ◯ 7 = 14

    15 ◯ 8 = 7   12 ◯ 9 = 3

    16 ◯ 6 = 10   17 ◯ 3 = 20

2. Write a number sentence for each set.

    | 12, 8, 4, =, + |

    | 9, 14, 5, +, = |

    _____

    | 7, 9, 16, −, = |

    | 8, 13, 5, −, = |

    _____

3. Write 4 number sentences for each picture.

7	+	6	=	13		13	−	6	=	7

☐ ○ ☐ = ☐   ☐ ○ ☐ = ☐

☐ ○ ☐ = ☐   ☐ ○ ☐ = ☐

☐ ○ ☐ = ☐   ☐ ○ ☐ = ☐

EXERCISE 49

1. There are many addition and subtraction sentences in
   the puzzle below.
   Find as many of them as you can.
   Two examples are given.

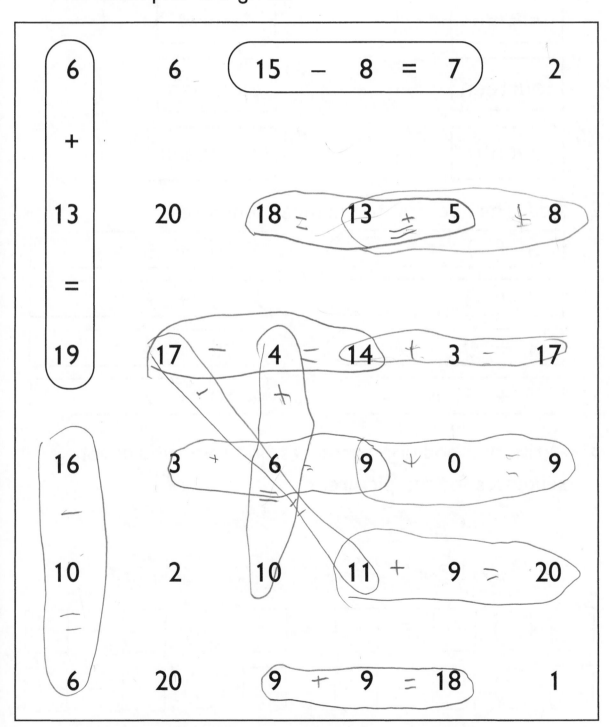

6	6	15 – 8 = 7	2
+			
13	20	18 13 5 8	
=			
19	17 – 4 = 14 3 – 17		
16	3 + 6 9 0 9		
10	2	10 11 + 9 = 20	
6	20	9 + 9 = 18	1

REVIEW 4

1. Write the numbers.

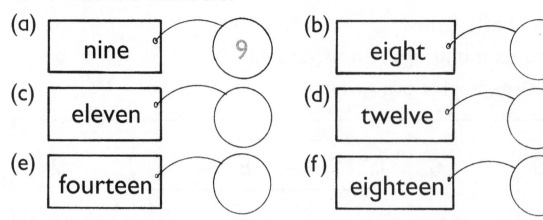

(a) nine — 9

(b) eight — ◯

(c) eleven — ◯

(d) twelve — ◯

(e) fourteen — ◯

(f) eighteen — ◯

(g) twenty — ◯

(h) seventeen — ◯

2. Add. Then pair up the number sentences.

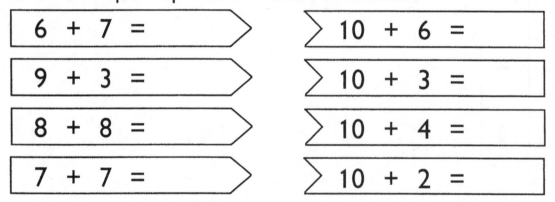

6 + 7 =	10 + 6 =
9 + 3 =	10 + 3 =
8 + 8 =	10 + 4 =
7 + 7 =	10 + 2 =

3. Write two addition sentences and two subtraction sentences for the picture.

☐ ◯ ☐ = ☐   ☐ ◯ ☐ = ☐

☐ ◯ ☐ = ☐   ☐ ◯ ☐ = ☐

4. Fill in the missing numbers.

(a)

| 10 | | | | 14 | | | 17 | | 19 | |

(b)

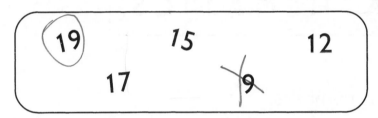

20 19 18 17 16 15 14 13 12 11

5. (a) Circle the greatest number.
   (b) Cross out the smallest number.

19   15   12

17   9

6. What comes next?

(a)

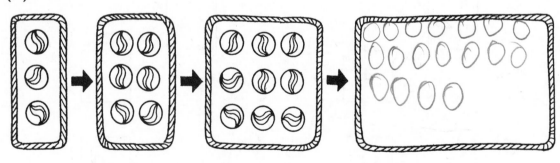

(b)

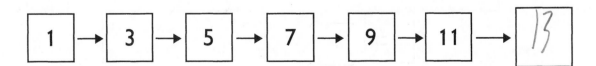

| 1 | → | 3 | → | 5 | → | 7 | → | 9 | → | 11 | → | 13 |

117

7. Fill in **1st**, **2nd**, **3rd** and **4th** to show the order.

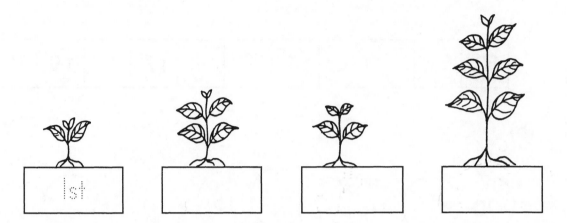

1st

8. Circle the 4th letter of this word:

| MATHEMATICS |

9. Write the missing numbers.

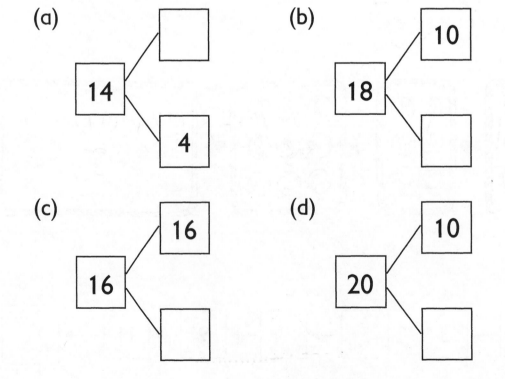

(a)

14 — 4

(b)

18 — 10

(c)

16 — 16

(d)

20 — 10

10. Samy has 14 stamps.

He buys 5 more.

How many stamps does he have now?

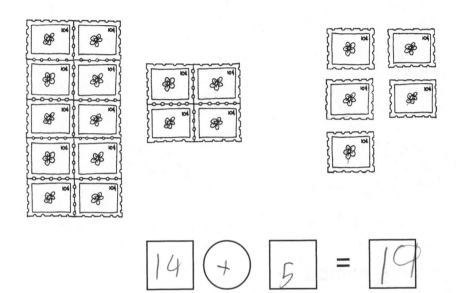

$$\boxed{14} \; \bigoplus \; \boxed{5} \; = \; \boxed{19}$$

He has __19__ stamps now.

11. There are 12 ducks.

4 are swimming.

How many ducks are not swimming?

$$\boxed{12} \; \bigominus \; \boxed{8} \; = \; \boxed{4}$$

__4__ ducks are not swimming.

REVIEW 5

1. Add.

   (a)

   $$10 + 5 = 15$$

   (b)

   $$10 + 10 = 20$$

2. Fill in the missing numbers.

   (a)

   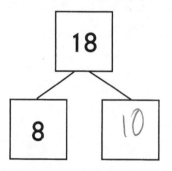

   (b)

   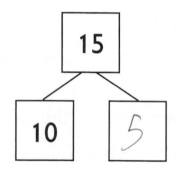

   (c) 14 is ___10___ and 4.

   (d) 12 is 10 and ___2___ .

3. Fill in the missing number.

   (a)

   (b)

   17 | 18 | 19 | 20

   (c)

   (d)

   12 | 14 | 16 | 18

4. Fill in the blanks.

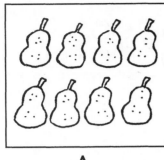 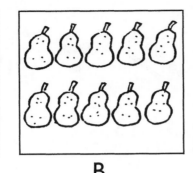 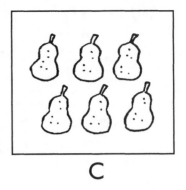

| A | B | C |

(a) Set ___B___ has the greatest number of pears.

(b) Set ___c___ has the smallest number of pears.

5. Add or subtract.

(a)

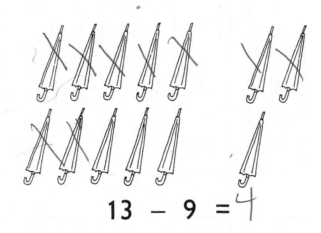

$8 + 5 = 11$

(b)

$13 - 9 = 4$

6. Complete the number sentences.

(a) $7 + 3 = 10$ (b) $10 - 8 = 2$

    $7 + 4 = 11$ $11 - 8 = 3$

    $7 + 5 = 12$ $12 - 8 = 4$

7. Write the missing numbers.

(a)

 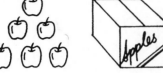 

$$6 + \boxed{8} = 13$$

(b)

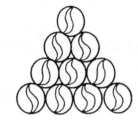 

$$14 - 3 = \boxed{10}$$

8. Write the missing number in each set.

(a)

4	6	7	14	7	9	
3	2	9	5	8		6
7	8	16			9	12

(b)

5	9	12	15	11	16	
2	3	9	9	7		4
3	6	3			6	10

9. Matthew had 12 cookies.
   He ate 5 of them.
   How many cookies did
   he have left?

   $\square \bigcirc \square = \square$

   He had _____ cookies left.

---

10. Joe has 14 pencils.
    He buys 3 more.
    How many pencils does he have now?

    $\square \bigcirc \square = \square$

    He has _____ pencils now.

---

11. Dani and Matthew have 15 books altogether.
    Dani has 8 books.
    How many books does
    Matthew have?

    $\square \bigcirc \square = \square$

    Matthew has _____ books.

EXERCISE 50

1. Color the shape that matches the object.

button	△	□	○	▭
envelope	△	□	○	▭
stamp 10¢	△	□	○	▭
7	△	□	○	▭
bag	△	□	○	▭
clock	△	□	○	▭
plate	△	□	○	▭

2. Color the shape that fits the shaded part.

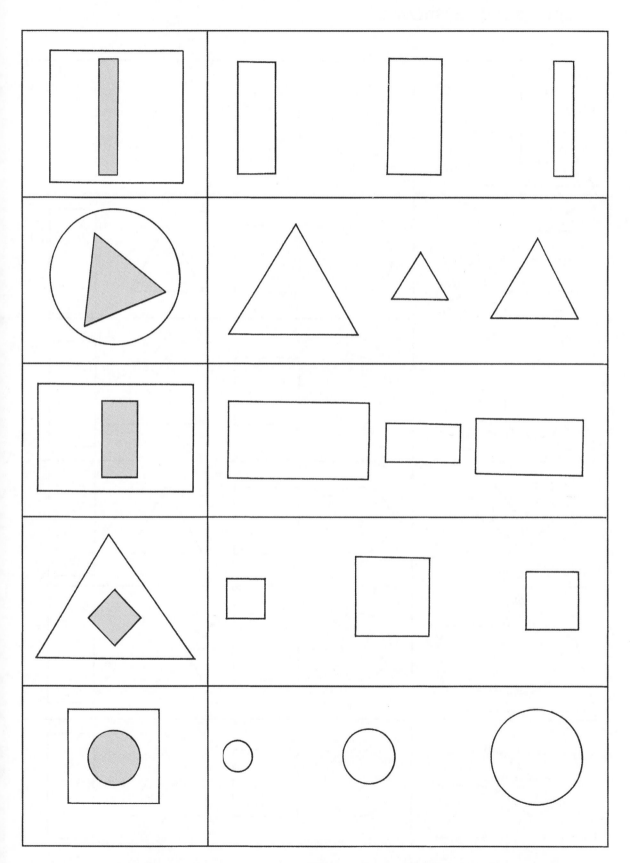

3. Color the shape that you can get by drawing around each solid as shown.

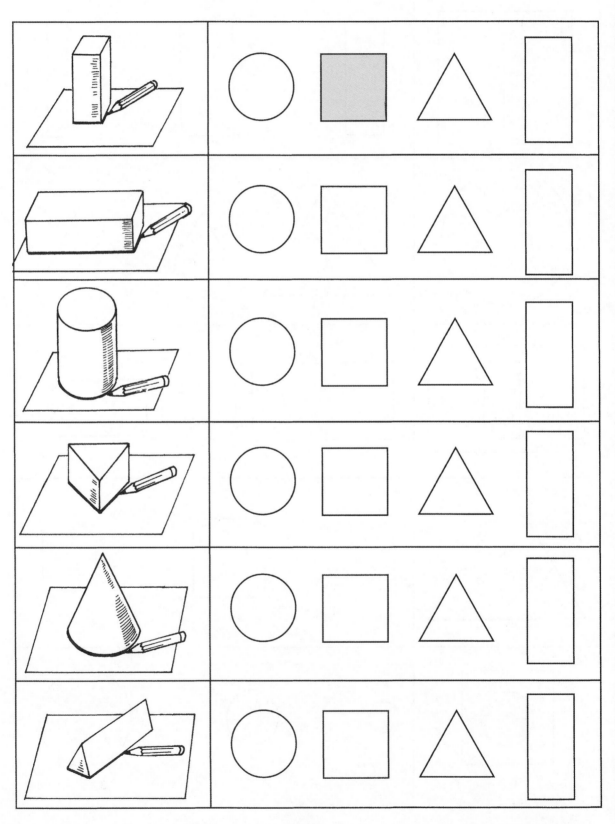

EXERCISE 51

1. Match the shaded face of each object to the correct shape.

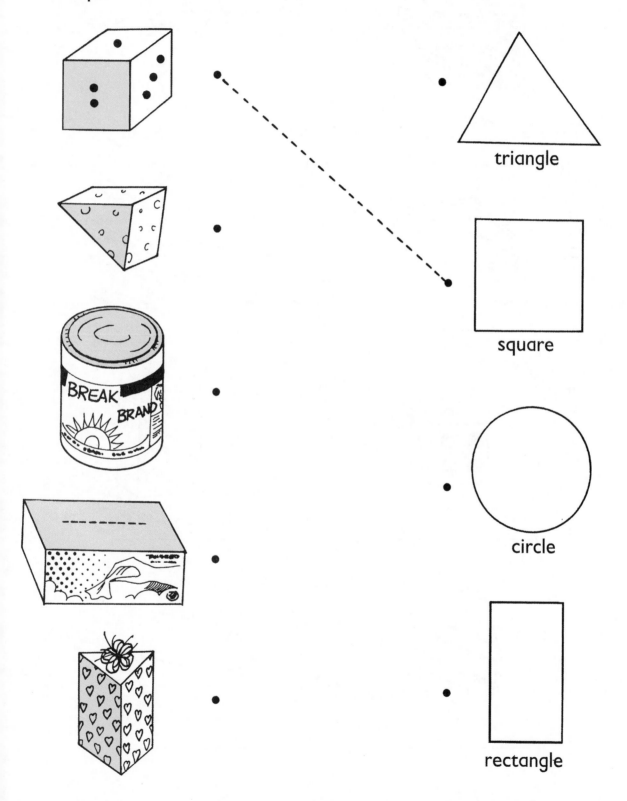

triangle

square

circle

rectangle

2. Name the shape of the shaded face.

(a)

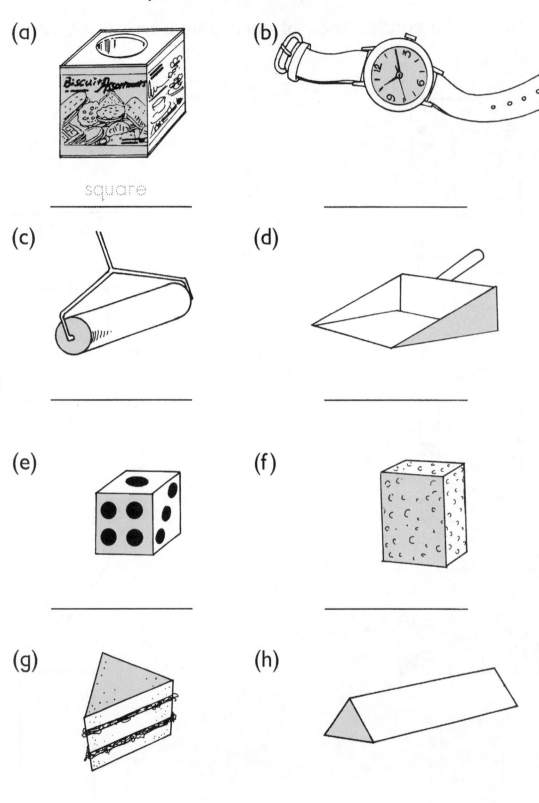

square
_____

(b)

_____

(c)

_____

(d)

_____

(e)

_____

(f)

_____

(g)

_____

(h)

_____

3. Color in this way:

squares — blue
rectangles — yellow
triangles — red
circles — green

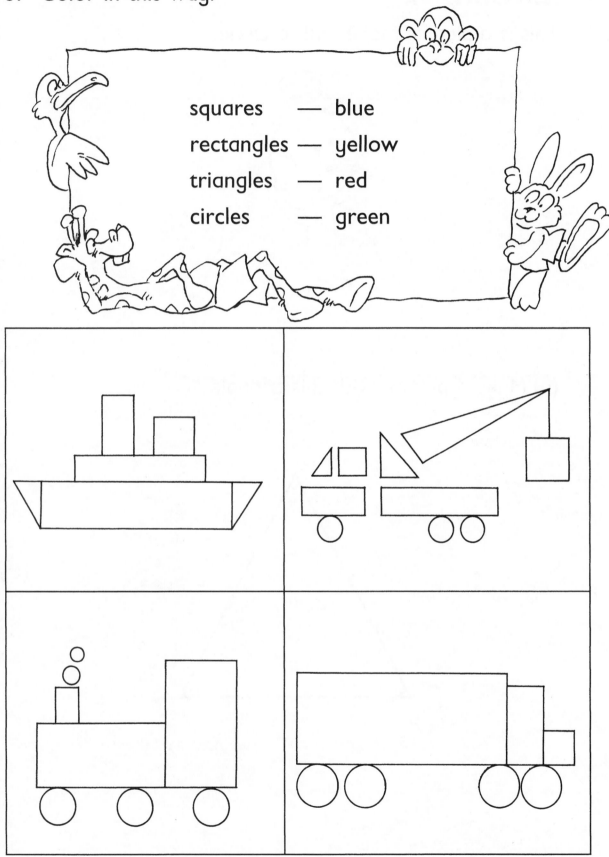

EXERCISE 52

1. This is a picture made with a circle.

(a) Make a picture with this triangle.

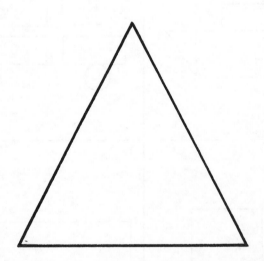

(b) Make a picture with these circles.

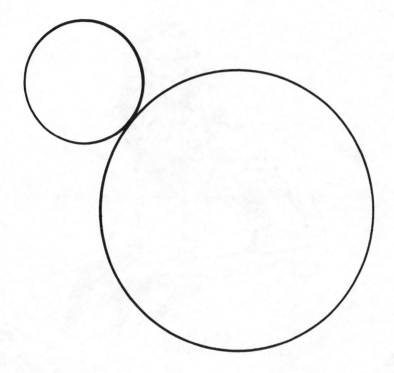

2. Draw a square by joining the dots. You will separate the 5 animals.

EXERCISE 53

1. Draw a smaller rectangle.

2. Draw a bigger triangle.

3. Draw a smaller circle.

4. Draw a bigger square.

5. Color the smallest shape red.

Color the biggest shape blue.

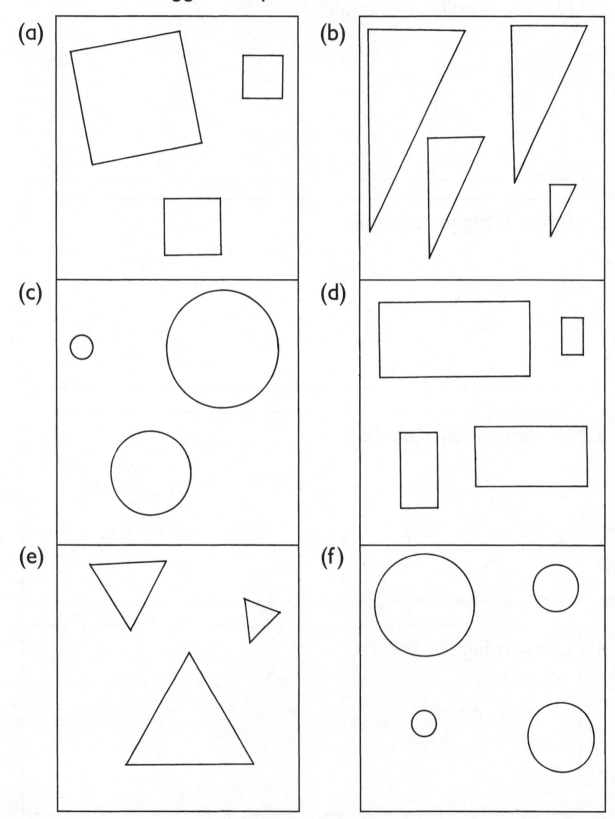

(a) (b) (c) (d) (e) (f)

EXERCISE 54

1. Study each pattern.

   Then color the shape that comes next.

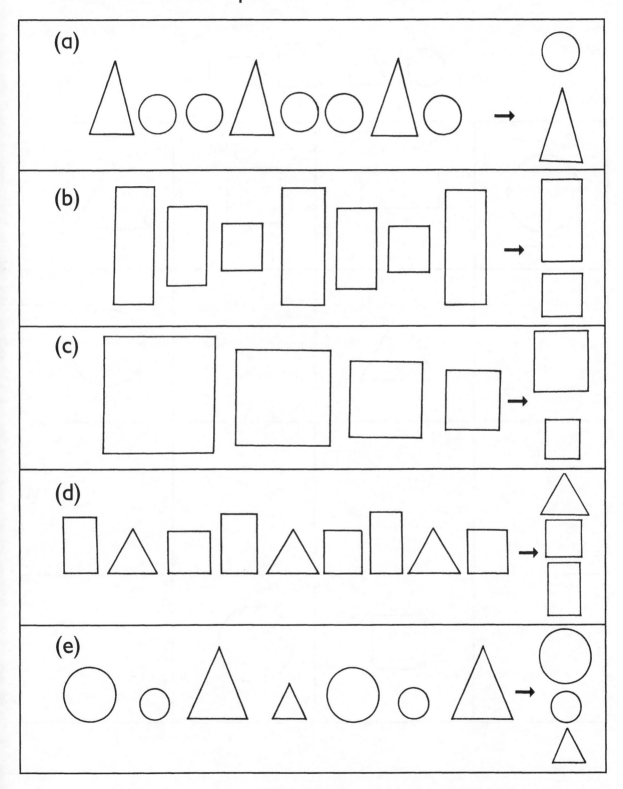

2. Draw and complete the pattern below.

   Each row (⟷) or column (↕) must have all these 4 shapes:

   ○ △ ☐ ▭

○	▭	☐	△
	△		○
	☐	○	

EXERCISE 55

1. Trace this square on a piece of paper and cut it into 4 triangles.

    Use the 4 triangles to form each of the shapes below.

    Draw dotted lines to show how it is done.

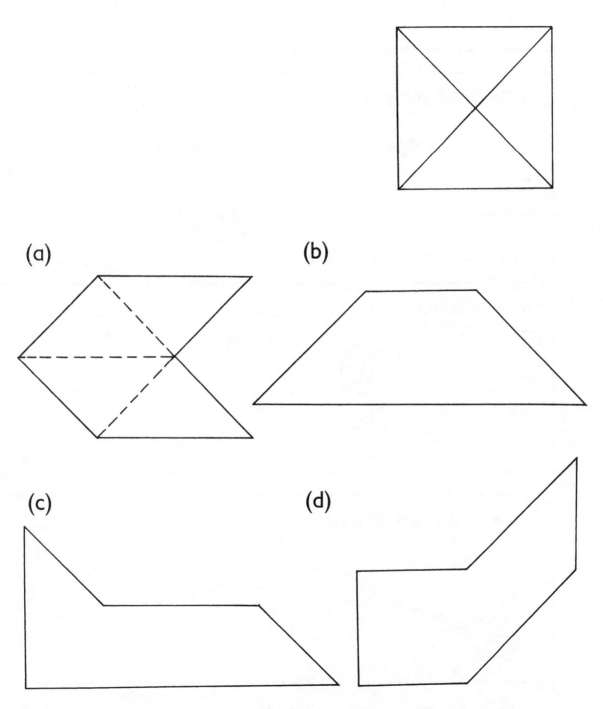

(a)

(b)

(c)

(d)

EXERCISE 56

1. Draw a shorter nail.

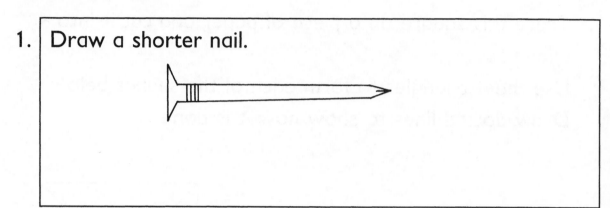

2. Draw a longer pencil.

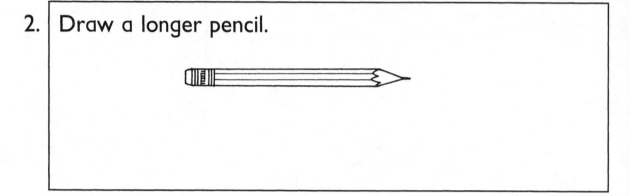

3. Draw a taller tree.

4. Draw a shorter arrow.

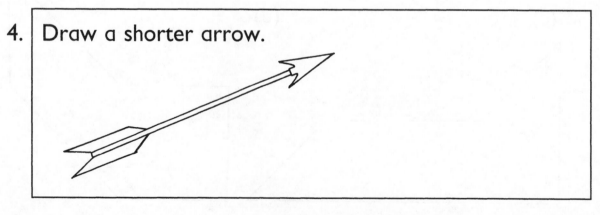

5. Color the longest bean.

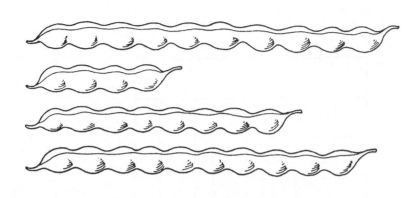

6. Color the tallest animal.

7. Color the shortest string of beads.

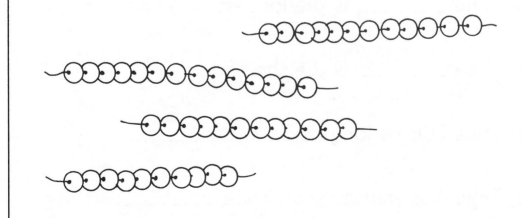

EXERCISE 57

1. Fill in the blanks.

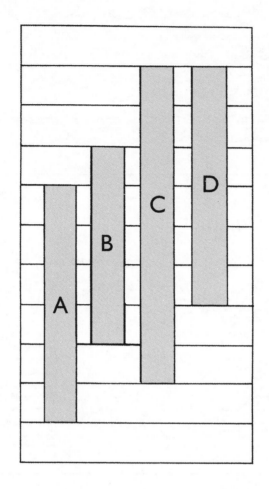

(a) Tape _____ is the longest.

(b) Tape _____ is the shortest.

(c) Tape D is as long as Tape _____.

(d) Tape A is shorter than Tape _____.

2. The paper tapes below measure the heights of the figures.
   Write the letter of each figure on the correct paper tape.

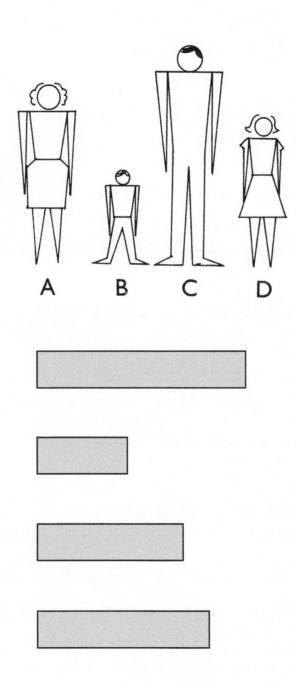

EXERCISE 58

1. Fill in the blanks.

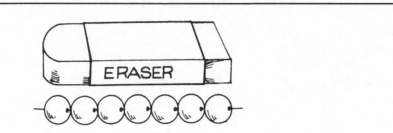

The eraser is as long as _____ beads.

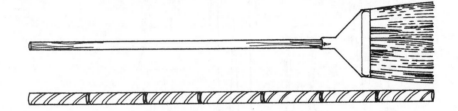

The broom is as long as _____ straws.

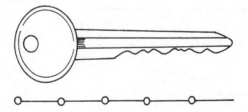

The key is as long as _____ pins.

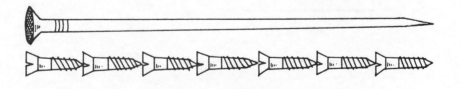

The nail is as long as _____ screws.

2. Fill in the blanks.

Use ▭━━━● as 1 unit.

The length of the pen is _____ units.

Use ▭▷ as 1 unit.

The length of the spoon is _____ units.

Use ▭ as 1 unit.

The length of the tube is _____ units.

3. Color the tape which is 8 units long.

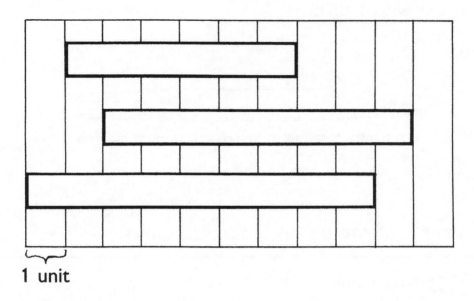

1 unit

4.

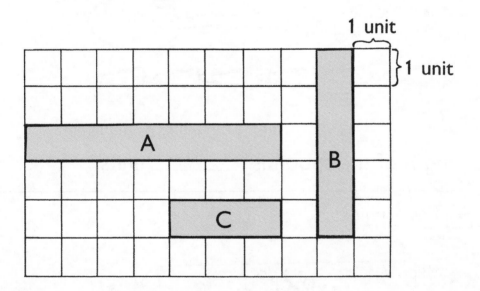

1 unit

1 unit

(a) Tape A is _____ units long.

(b) Tape B is _____ units long.

(c) Tape C is _____ units long.

EXERCISE 59

1. Write **heavier than**, **lighter than** or **as heavy as**.

(a)

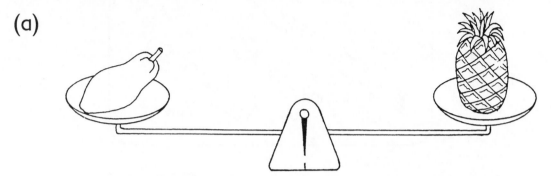

The papaya is _____ the pineapple.

(b)

The crab is _____ the fish.

(c)

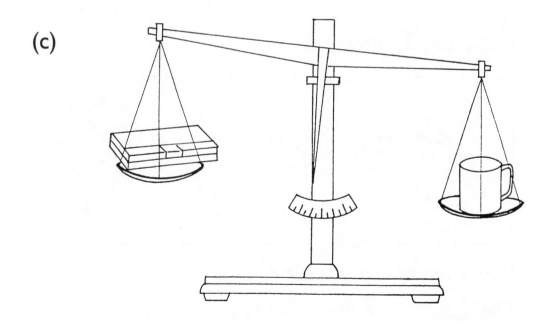

The pencil box is _____ the mug.

2. (a) Get these 2 things:

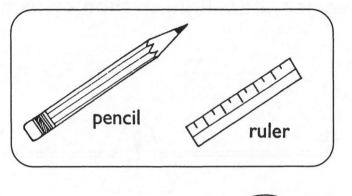

Use a balance to compare their weights.

The _____ is heavier than the _____ .

(b) Get these 3 things:

Use a balance to compare their weights.

The _____ is the heaviest.

The _____ is the lightest.

EXERCISE 60

1. (a) Use ⊙ as 1 unit.

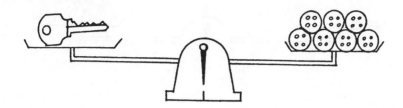

The key weighs _____ units.

(b) Use ◐ as 1 unit.

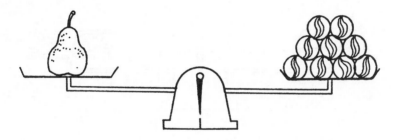

The pear weighs _____ units.

(c) Use ◯ as 1 unit.

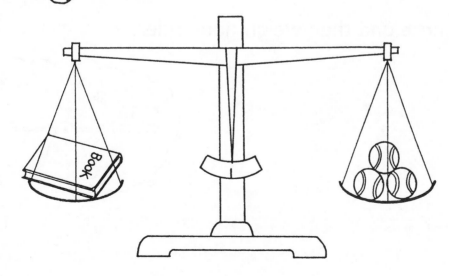

The book weighs _____ units.

2. (a) Use 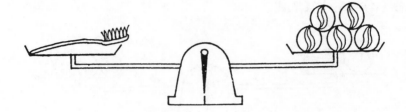 as 1 unit.

The toothbrush weighs _____ units.

(b) Use ⊲⊏ as 1 unit.

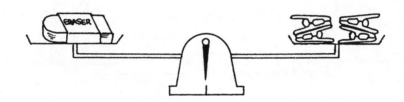

The eraser weighs _____ units.

3. Use ◁⊐ as 1 unit.

Estimate and then weigh your ruler.

My ruler weighs about _____ units.

EXERCISE 61

1. Use  as 1 unit.

(a) The papaya weighs _____ units.

(b) The watermelon weighs _____ units.

(c) The pineapple weighs _____ units.

(d) The _____ is the heaviest.

(e) The _____ is the lightest.

(f) The pineapple is lighter than the _____.

2. Use 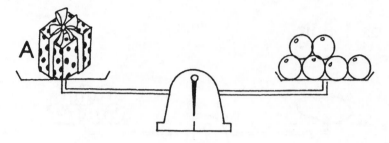 as 1 unit.

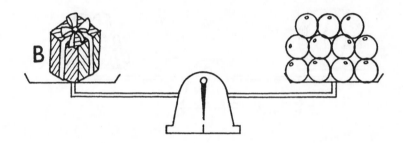

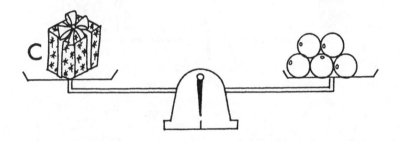

(a) Box A weighs _____ units.

(b) Box B weighs _____ units.

(c) Box C weighs _____ units.

(d) Box A is heavier than Box _____ .

(e) Box _____ is the lightest.

(f) Box _____ is the heaviest.

REVIEW 6

1. Write the numbers.

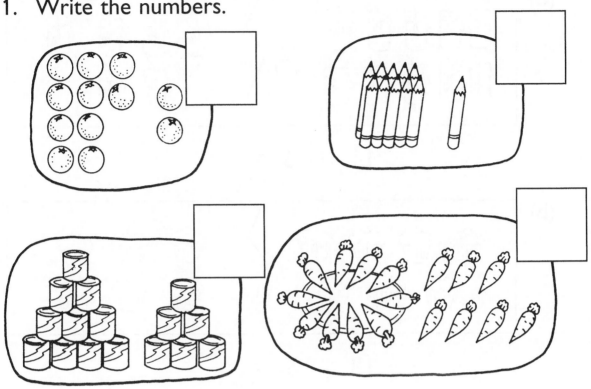

2. Match the numbers and words.

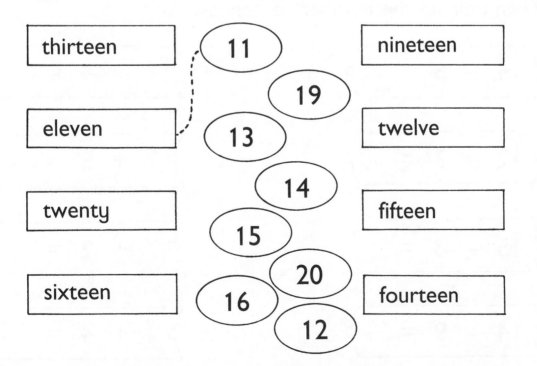

3. Add or subtract.

(a)

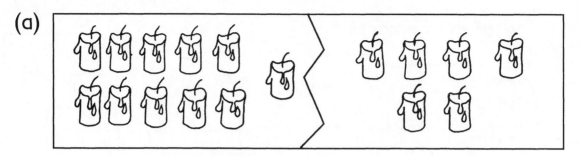

$$11 + 6 =$$

(b)

$$13 - 6 =$$

4. Add or subtract.
Then pair up the number sentences.

14 – 6 =

12 – 3 =

15 – 8 =

14 – 9 =

1 + 4 =

2 + 5 =

7 + 2 =

4 + 4 =

5. Color the triangle which has the same size as the shaded one.

6. Fill in the blanks.

(a)

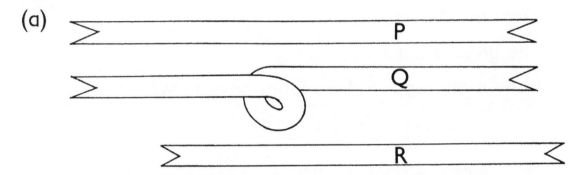

_____ is the shortest ribbon.

_____ is the longest ribbon.

(b)

_____ is the tallest child.

_____ is the shortest child.

_____ is taller than A.

7. Mary had 19 buttons.

   She used 5 of them for a dress.

   How many buttons did she have left?

   $\square \bigcirc \square = \square$

   She had _____ buttons left.

---

8. Dani has 12 apples.

   She gives 8 apples to Lily.

   How many apples does Dani have now?

   $\square \bigcirc \square = \square$

   She has _____ apples now.

---

9. Jerome has 8 shells.

   John gives him 7 more.

   How many shells does Jerome have now?

   $\square \bigcirc \square = \square$

   He has _____ shells now.

REVIEW 7

1. Count and write the numbers in words.

   (a)

   (b)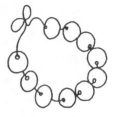

   _____   _____

2. (a) Color 3 watermelons.

   (b) Color the 3rd pineapple from the left.

3. Arrange the numbers in order. Begin with the smallest.

   | 6 | 14 | 3 | 11 | 7 |

   _____ , _____ , _____ , _____ , _____ ,
   smallest   greatest

155

4. Write the missing numbers.

(a)

 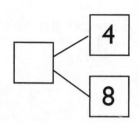

(b)

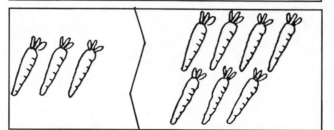 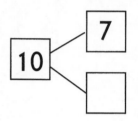

5. Add or subtract.

(a)

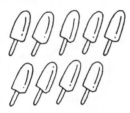 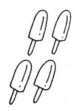

$$9 + 4 =$$

(b)

$$12 - 7 =$$

6. Add or subtract.

(a) $3 + 6 =$ (b) $8 - 7 =$

(c) $5 + 5 =$ (d) $10 - 2 =$

(e) $12 + 4 =$ (f) $16 - 3 =$

(g) $6 + 8 =$ (h) $17 - 8 =$

7. Fill in the blanks.

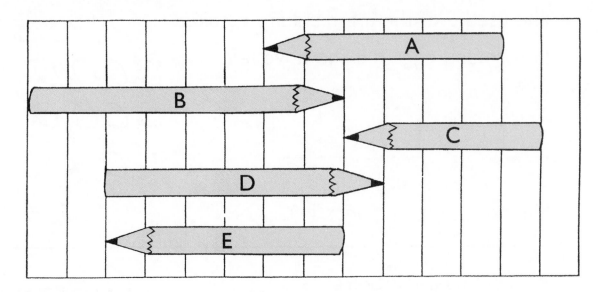

(a) Pencil _____ is as long as pencil _____ .

(b) Pencil _____ is the shortest.

(c) Pencil _____ is the longest.

8. Cross out the one which does not belong.

9. Color the 2 pieces that make up the given shape.

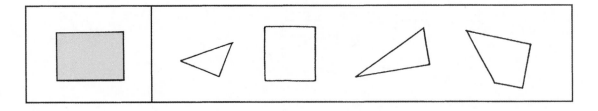

10. Mary had 10 eggs.

    She used 6 of them for baking a cake.

    How many eggs did she have left?

    □ ○ □ = □

    She had _____ eggs left.

---

11. Ashley had 14 stickers.

    She gave some of them to Lily.

    She had 7 stickers left.

    How many stickers did she give to Lily?

    □ ○ □ = □

    She gave _____ stickers to Lily.

---

12. Emily needs 16 chairs for a party.

    She has 9 chairs now.

    How many more chairs does she need?

    □ ○ □ = □

    She needs _____ more chairs.